THE REAL ★ BOOK OF JAZZ

WISE PUBLICATIONS
London/New York/Paris/Sydney/Copenhagen/Madrid

CW00802495

Contents

A Foggy Day

Music & Lyrics by George Gershwin & Ira Gershwin

A Night In Tunisia

Music by Frank Paparelli & John 'Dizzy' Gillespie ★ Words by Raymond Leveen

A Taste Of Honey

Words by Ric Marlow ★ Music by Bobby Scott

Medium jazz waltz

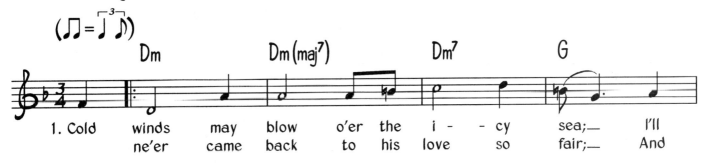

1. Cold winds may blow o'er the i - cy sea;— I'll
ne'er came back to his love so fair;— And

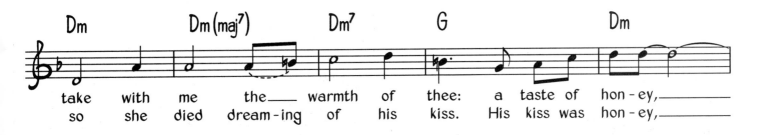

take with me the— warmth of thee: a taste of hon-ey,—
so she died dream-ing of his kiss. His kiss was hon-ey,—

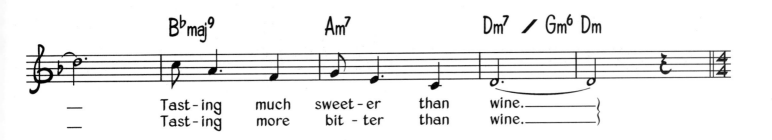

Tast-ing much sweet-er than wine.—
Tast-ing more bit-ter than wine.—

I will re - turn,— I will re - turn. I'll come

back for the hon-ey— and you.— 2. He you.—

Afternoon In Paris

By John Lewis

Ain't Misbehavin'

Words by Andy Razaf ★ Music by Thomas Waller & Harry Brooks

All Of Me

Words & Music by Seymour Simons & Gerald Marks

Medium bounce

C ... **E7**
All of me, why not take all of me?

A7 ... **Dm**
Can't you see I'm no good with - out you?

E7 ... **Am**
Take my lips, I want to lose them.

D7 ... **Dm7** **G7**
Take my arms, I'll nev - er use them.

C ... **E7**
Your good- bye left me with eyes that cry.

A7 ... **Dm**
How can I go on, dear, with - out you?

F6 ... **Fm6** **Cmaj7** **A9**
You took the part that once was my heart, So

D9 **G13** **C** **Fm6/C** **C**
why not take all of me?

All The Things You Are

Music by Jerome Kern ★ Words by Oscar Hammerstein II

All The Cats Join In

Music by Eddie Sauter ★ Words by Ray Gilbert & Alec Wilder

Medium bounce

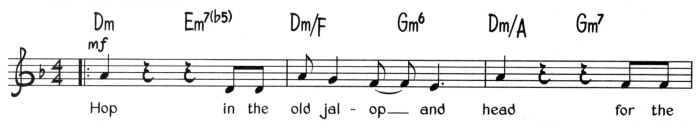

Hop in the old jal - op__ and head for the

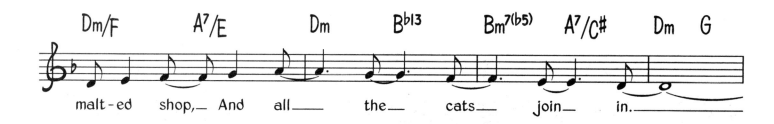

malt - ed shop,__ And all__ the__ cats__ join__ in.__

__ Down goes my last two - bit,__ comes up one ba-

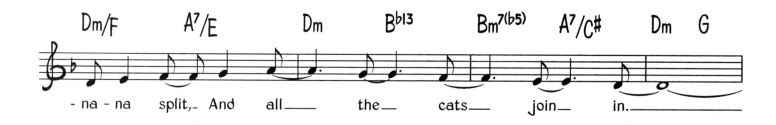

-na - na split,__ And all__ the__ cats__ join__ in.__

Drop your jack in the old juke-box, play your fa-vour-ite

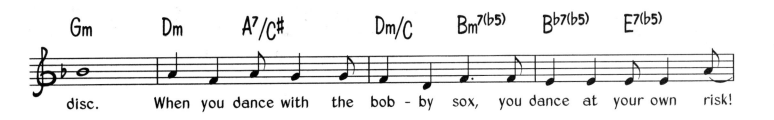

disc. When you dance with the bob-by sox, you dance at your own risk!

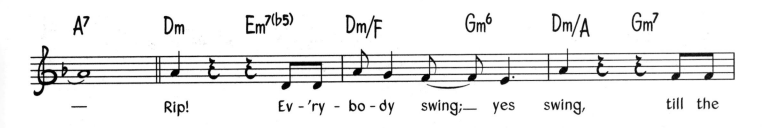

— Rip! Ev-'ry-bo-dy swing;— yes swing, till the

raf-ters ring,— And all____ the__ cats__ join__ in.__

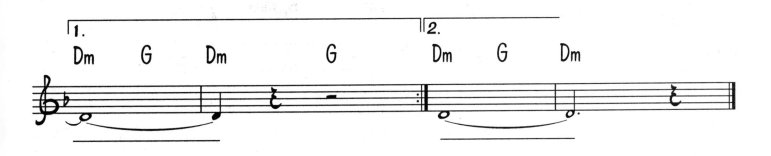

13

Alright, Okay, You Win

Words & Music by Sid Wyche & Mayme Watts

Medium swing

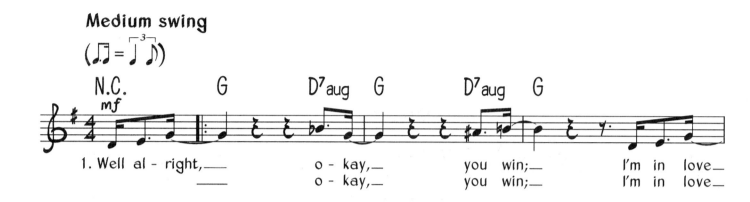

1. Well al - right,___ o - kay,___ you win;___ I'm in love___
___ o - kay,___ you win;___ I'm in love___

— with you.__ Well al - right,__ o - kay,__ you win;_____ Ba - by
— with you.__ Well al - right,__ o - kay,__ you win;_____ Ba - by

what can I do?__ I'll__ do an - y - thing__ you say;__ It's
what can I do?__ An - y - thing you say__ I'll__ do;__ As

just got - ta be that way.__ 2. Well al - right, All that__ I am ask-
long as it's me and you.__ ___

- ing,   all I want from you;—   Just love— me like

I love— you an' it won't be hard to do.—   Well al - right—

— o - kay,—   you win;—   I'm in love— with you.— Well al - right,—

— o - kay,—   you win;—   Ba - by what can I do?— I'll—

— do an - y - thing— you say;—   It's just got - ta be that way!

Anthropology

By Dizzy Gillespie & Charlie Parker

Medium fast

American Patrol

Composed by F.W. Meacham

April In Paris

Words & Music by E.Y. Harburg & Vernon Duke

Au Privave

By Charlie Parker

Baby Won't You Please Come Home

Words & Music by Charles Warfield & Clarence Williams

Ba - by, won't you please come home, 'Cos your mam - ma's all a -

- lone? I have tried, in vain, Nev-er no more to call your name.

When you left you broke my heart, Be -

- cause I nev - er thought we'd part. Ev - 'ry hour in the day you will

hear me say, Ba - by, won't you please come home?

home? Dad - dy needs mam - ma. Ba - by won't you please come home?

Baby Elephant Walk

Music by Henry Mancini ★ Words by Hal David

Bakiff

By Juan Tizol

Medium fast

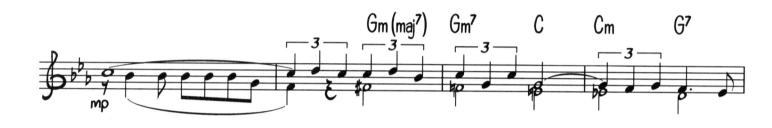

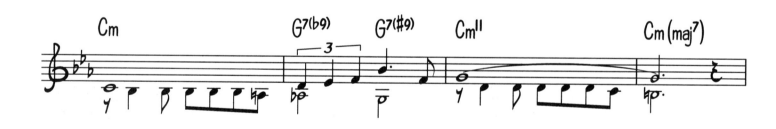

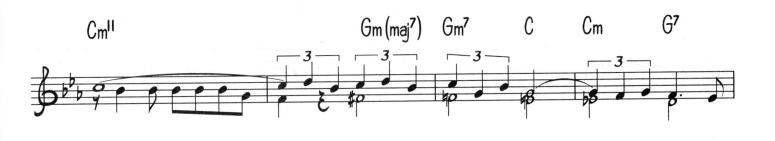

Bark For Barksdale

By Gerry Mulligan

Baubles, Bangles And Beads

Words & Music by Robert Wright & George Forrest

Be-Bop

By John 'Dizzy' Gillespie

Beat Me Daddy, Eight To The Bar

Words & Music Don Raye, Hughie Prince & Eleanore Sheehy

Bernie's Tune

By Bernie Miller

Between The Devil And The Deep Blue Sea

Words by Ted Koehler ★ Music by Harold Arlen

Bill Bailey Won't You Please Come Home

Traditional

Bird Feathers

By Charlie Parker

Blue Haze

By Miles Davis

Boogie Woogie Bugle Boy

Words & Music by Don Raye & Hughie Prince

Medium Boogie Woogie

He was a fa-mous trum-pet man from out Chi-ca-go way,— He

had a boo-gie style that no one else could play.— He was the top man of his craft—

— But then his num-ber came up,— and he was gone with the draft.— He's in the

ar-my now a-blow-in' re-veil-le; He's the Boo-gie Woo-gie Bu-gle Boy of

Com-pa-ny B.— They made him blow a bu-gle for his Un-cle Sam;— It
puts the boys to sleep with boo-gie ev-'ry night, And

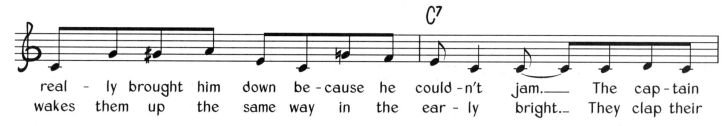

real-ly brought him down be-cause he could-n't jam.— The cap-tain
wakes them up the same way in the ear-ly bright.— They clap their

But Beautiful

Words by Johnny Burke ★ Music by Jimmy Van Heusen

Medium slow

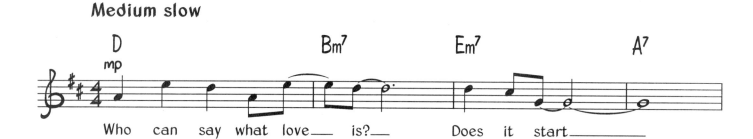

Who can say what love___ is?___ Does it start___

in the mind___ or the heart?___

When I hear dis - cus - sions on what love is,___

Ev - 'ry - bo - dy speaks a dif - f'rent part.___ Love is

fun - ny___ or it's sad,___ Or it's qui - et___ or it's mad.___ It's a

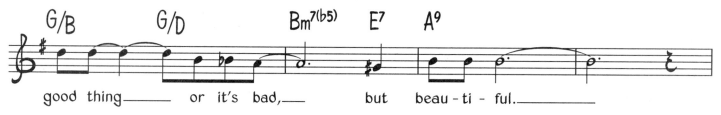

good thing___ or it's bad,___ but beau - ti - ful.___

Beau-ti-ful to take a chance and, if you fall, you fall; And I'm

think-ing I would-n't mind at all. Love is

tear-ful or it's gay, It's a prob-lem or it's play; It's a

prob-lem ei-ther way, but beau-ti-ful. And I'm

think-ing if you were mine I'd nev-er let you go; And

rit.

that would be but beau-ti-ful I know.

Buck Dance

By Woody Herman & Nat Pierce

44

Call Me Irresponsible

Words by Sammy Cahn ★ Music by Jimmy Van Heusen

Cantiga Nova Swing

By Dave Brubeck

Caravan

By Duke Ellington, Irving Mills & Juan Tizol

Fast

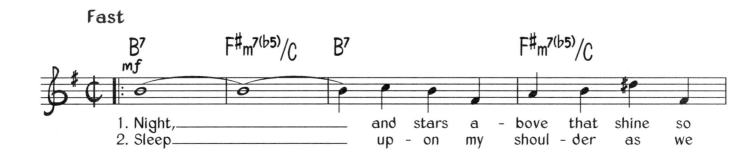

1. Night,_____ and stars a - bove that shine so
2. Sleep_____ up - on my shoul - der as we

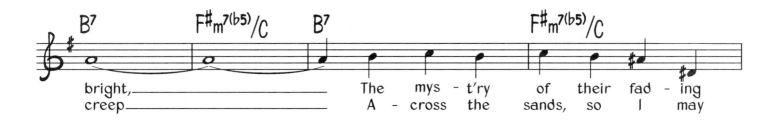

bright,_____ The mys - t'ry of their fad - ing
creep_____ A - cross the sands, so I may

light_____ that shines up - on our ca - ra -
keep_____ This mem - 'ry of our ca - ra -

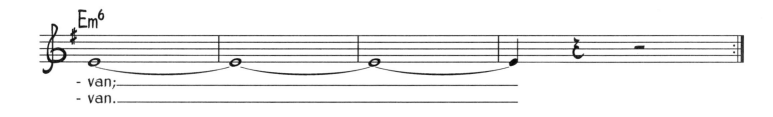

- van;_____
- van._____

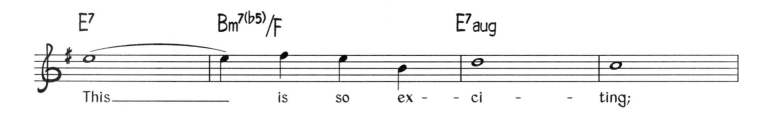

This_____ is so ex - ci - - ting;

You _____ are so in - vi - -ting,

Rest - - -ing in my arms As I

thrill to _____ the mag - ic charms _____ of

You _____ be - side me here be - neath the

blue; _____ My dream of love is com - ing

true _____ With - in our des - ert ca - ra -

- van. _____

Chattanoogie Shoe Shine Boy

Words & Music by Henry Stone & Jack Strapp

Medium fast

Have you ev - er passed the cor - ner of Fourth and Grand,__ Where a lit - tle ball of rhy - thm has a shoe - shine stand?__ Peo - ple ga - ther round and they clap__ their hand;__ He's a great big bun - dle of joy.__ He pops a boo - gie woo - gie rag, the Chat - ta - noo - gie shoe - shine boy.__ He charg - es you a nick - el just to shine one shoe;__ He makes the old - est kind of leath - er look like new.__ You feel as tho' you want to dance when he gets thro';__ He's a great big bun - dle of joy.__ He pops a boo - gie woo - gie rag, the

F/G … C F⁷ C C⁷ F

Chat-ta-noo-gie shoe-shine boy_____ It's a won-der that the

C D⁷

rag don't tear, the way he makes it pop.— You ought to see him

G⁷

fan the air— with his hop-pi-ty hip-pi-ty hip-pi-ty hop-pi-ty hop-pi-ty hip-pi-ty hop! He

C

o-pens up for bus-'ness when the clock strike's nine;— He likes to get 'em ear-ly when they're

C⁷ F⁷

feel-in' fine.— Ev-'ry-bo-dy gets a lit-tle rise— and shine— with the

C G⁷

great big bun-dle of joy.— He pops a boo-gie woo-gie rag, the

1. C F⁷ C G⁷   2. C F⁷ C

F/G

Chat-ta-noo-gie shoe-shine boy._____ Have you _____

Chicago

Words & Music by Fred Fisher

Clap Yo' Hands

Words & Music by George & Ira Gershwin

Come Fly With Me

Lyrics by Sammy Cahn ★ Music by James Van Heusen

up there,– I'll be hold-ing you so near,——

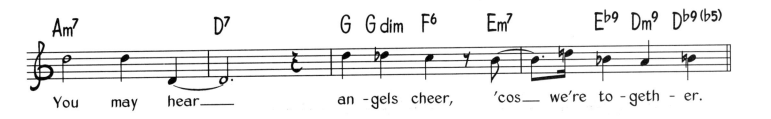

You may hear—— an-gels cheer, 'cos— we're to-geth-er.

Weath-er-wise,— it's such— a love-ly day!———————— Just

say the words and we'll beat the birds— down to A - ca-pul-co Bay. It's

per-fect for— a fly— -ing hon-ey-moon, they say. Come

fly with me!— Let's fly!— Let's fly— a - way!——

Crazy Rhythm

Words by Irving Caesar ★ Music by Joseph Meyer & Roger Wolfe Kahn

Cute

Words by Stanley Styne ★ Music by Neal Hefti

Mind if I say you're cute?

In ev-'ry way you're cute!

Those big blue eyes, that turned-up nose,

That cool and care-free pose.

I mean I like your style;

That sly in-trigu-ing smile.

Your ev-'ry mood, your at-ti-tude,

Just add up to you're cute!

Day In, Day Out

Words by Johnny Mercer ★ Music by Rube Bloom

Medium fast

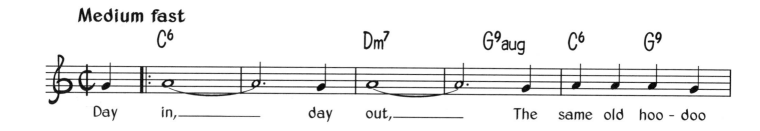

Day in,_____ day out,_____ The same old hoo - doo

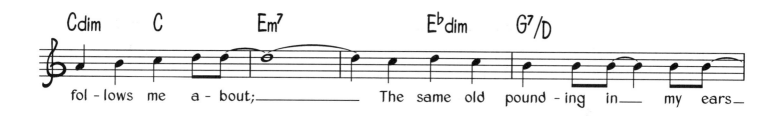

fol - lows me a - bout;_____ The same old pound - ing in__ my ears__

__ when - ev - er I think of you;_____ And, dar - ling, I think of you__

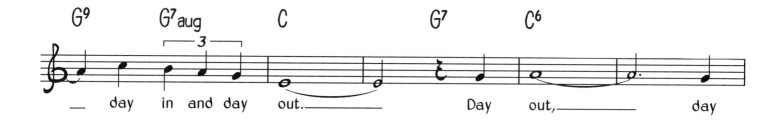

__ day in and day out._____ Day out,_____ day

in,_____ I need - n't tell you how my days be - gin!_____

__ When I a - wake, I a - wake with a tin - gle,__ One pos - si - bi - li - ty in

Dm⁷   G   Bm   Am⁹   D⁷aug   Dm⁷

view; That pos-si-bi-li-ty of may-be see - ing you._____

G⁹   G⁷aug   C⁶   Dm⁷   G⁹aug

_ Come rain,_____ come shine,_____ I

C⁶   G⁹   Cdim   C   E⁷aug E⁷   A⁷⁽ᵇ⁹⁾   A⁷aug

meet you and to me the day is fine._____ Then I

D⁷aug   D⁷   Fm⁶   G⁷aug   Cmaj⁷   A⁷aug

kiss your lips_____ and the pound-ing be - comes_____ The o - cean's roar,—

D¹³   Dm⁶   G⁷aug   Cmaj⁷   A⁷aug A⁷   D⁷

_____ a thou - sand drums!_____ Can't you see it's love?_____

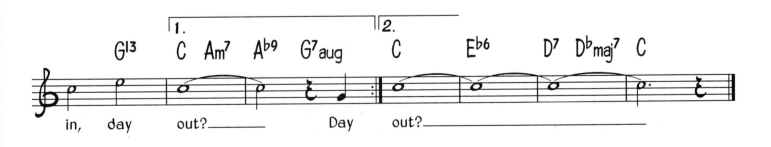

Fm⁶   G⁷aug   C⁶   A⁷   Dm⁷

_ Can there be an - y doubt,_____ When there it is, day

1. G¹³   C Am⁷ Aᵇ⁹ G⁷aug   C   2. Eᵇ⁶   D⁷ Dᵇmaj⁷ C

in, day out?_____ Day out?_____

Dixie Band Stomp

Words & Music by Joe Daniels & Stanley Butcher

Dizzy Atmosphere

By John 'Dizzy' Gillespie

Django

By John Lewis

Slow

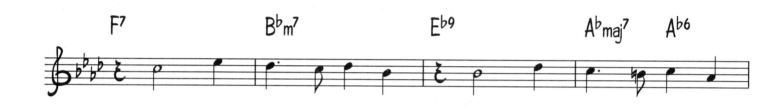

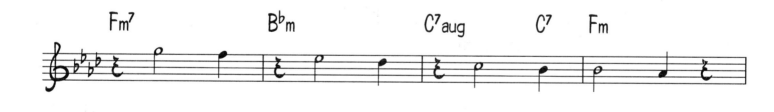

Do Nothin' 'Til You Hear From Me

Music by Duke Ellington ★ Words by Bob Russell

(Do) The Hucklebuck

Words by Roy Alfred ★ Music by Andy Gibson

Now here's a dance you should know,_ Hey! Ba-by, when the lights are down low. Hey! You rock your ba-by then go. Hey! You do the huck-le-buck, do the huck-le-buck; If you don't know how to do it, then you're out of luck. Shove your ba-by in, Twist her all a-round; Then you start a-twist-in' it and mov-in' all a-round. You wrig-gle like a snake, wad-dle like a duck; That's what you do when you do the huck-le-buck._____ Hey!

Don't Blame Me

Words & Music by Jimmy McHugh & Dorothy Fields

Drop Me Off In Harlem

Words by Nick Kenny ★ Music by Duke Ellington

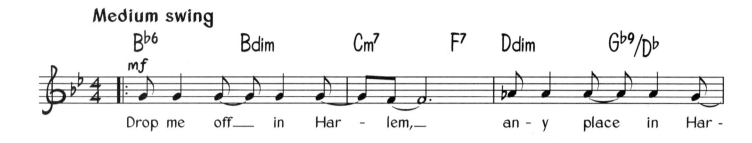

Drop me off__ in Har - lem,__ an - y place in Har -

- lem.__ There's some - one wait - ing there who makes it seem like

Hea - ven up in Har - lem.__ I don't want_ your Dix - ie,__

you can keep_ your Dix - ie.__ There's no one down in Dix - ie who can take me

'way from my own Har - lem.— Har-lem has_ those south-ern skies,_ they're

in my ba-by's smile;— I id-ol - ize_ my ba-by's eyes_ and

clas-sy up-town style. If Har-lem moved_ to Chi - na,— I

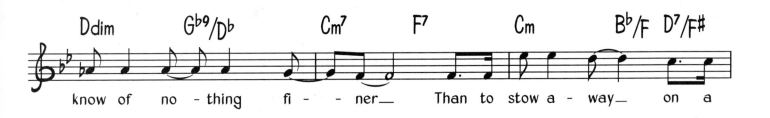

know of no - thing fi - - ner— Than to stow a - way_ on a

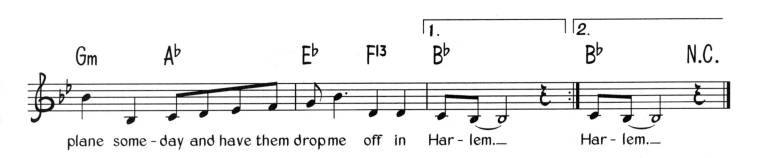

plane some - day and have them drop me off in Har - lem.— Har - lem.—

Drum Boogie

Words & Music by Gene Krupa & Roy Eldridge

(Boo-gie) You hear the rhy-thm romp-in'.___ (Boo-gie) You see the drum-mer

stomp-in'.___ Drum Boo-gie, Drum Boo-gie;

It real-ly is a kil-ler. Drum Boo-gie, Drum

Boo-gie; The Drum Boo-gie Woo-gie.___

East Of The Sun (And West Of The Moon)

Words & Music by Brooks Bowman

Easy To Love

Words & Music by Cole Porter

Everything But You

By Duke Ellington, Harry James & Don George

Medium bounce

1. You left me a horse from Tex-as,— A house with in-stal-ments due,—
left me some beans from Bos-ton,— A bi-cy-cle built for two,—

A let-ter with lots of x-s;— Ev-'ry-thing but you.— 2. You
A me-mo-ry to get lost in;— Ev-'ry-thing but you.— 2. You

Each day was so gay and so dar-ing,— I loved ev-'ry breath-

-tak-ing min-ute For how could I know— I was shar-ing a kiss with-out a

fu-ture in it? You left me a dream to room with,— A cof-fee pot from Pe-ru,

A knife and a fork to spoon with;— Ev-'ry-thing but you.—

Fascinating Rhythm

Music & Lyrics by George Gershwin & Ira Gershwin

Medium bounce

Flight Of The Foo Birds

By Neal Hefti

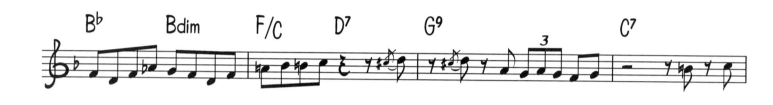

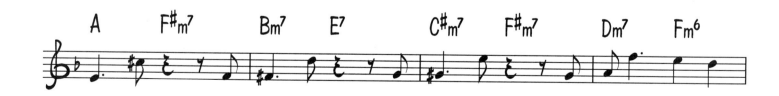

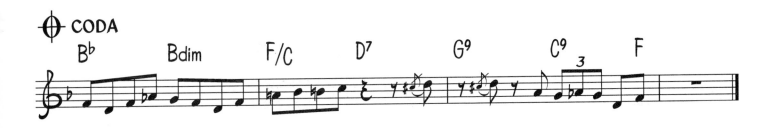

Fly Me To The Moon (In Other Words)

Words & Music by Bart Howard

Flying Home

By Benny Goodman & Lionel Hampton

Frenesi

English Words by Ray Charles & S.K. Russell ★ Music by Alberto Dominguez

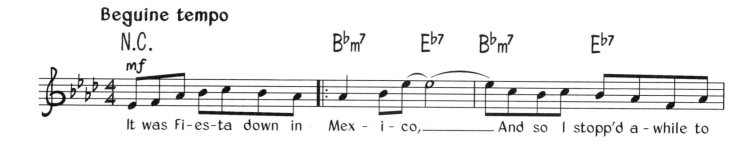

It was Fi-es-ta down in Mex-i-co,_____ And so I stopp'd a-while to

see the show._____ I knew that "Fre-ne-si" meant "Please love me",

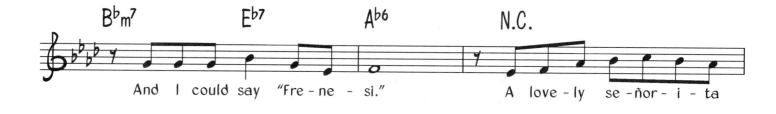

And I could say "Fre-ne-si." A love-ly se-ñor-i-ta

caught my eye;_____ I stood en-chant-ed as she wan-der'd by_____

_____ And, nev-er know-ing that it came from me, I gent-ly sigh'd "Fre-ne-

- si." She stopp'd and raised her eyes to mine, Her lips just plead ed to be

kissed; Her eyes were soft as can-dle-shine, So how was I to re-

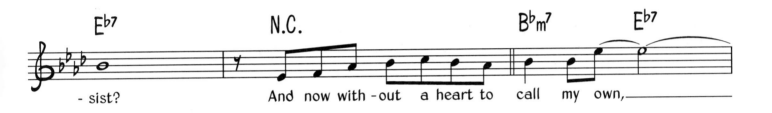

- sist? And now with-out a heart to call my own,

A great-er hap-pi-ness I've nev-er known, Be-cause her kiss-es are for

me a-lone. Who would-n't say "Fre-ne-si"? It was Fi-es-ta down in

- si?" Who would-n't say "Fre-ne-si"?

Four

By Miles Davis

Fast

Groovin' High

By John 'Dizzy' Gillespie

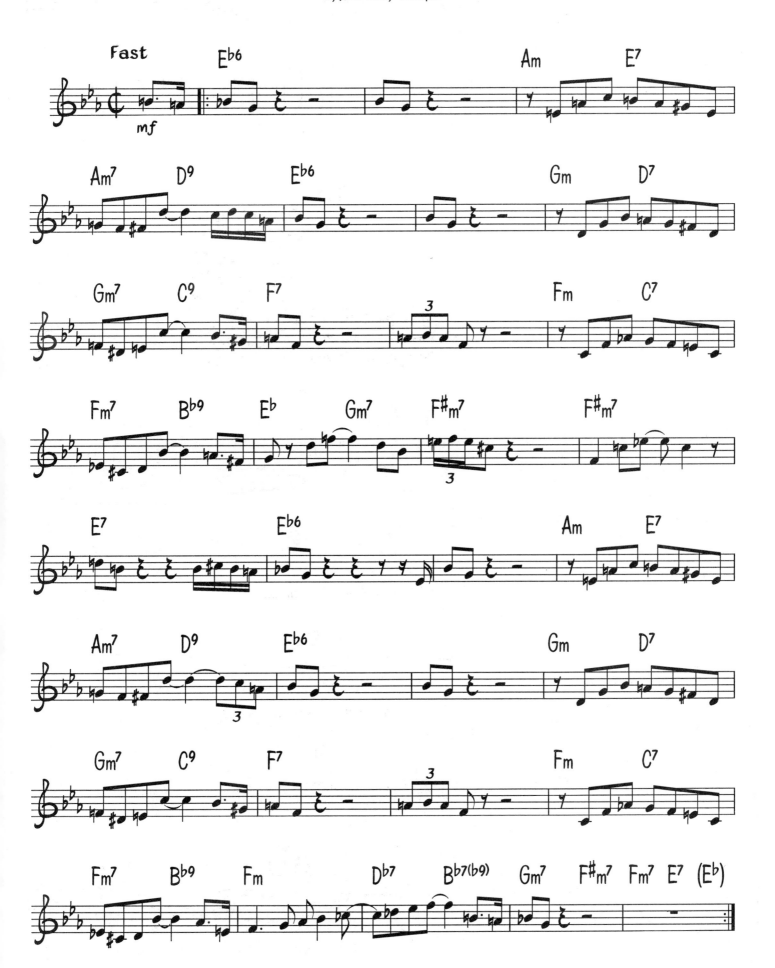

Get On Board, Little Children

Words & Music by Don Raye & Gene de Paul

Fast 'Gospel' swing

1. That right-eous train is com-in', you've got no time to lose; Ol'
   catch her as she pass-es, she'll take you an-y-where; No

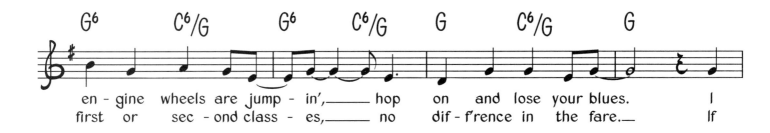

en-gine wheels are jump-in', hop on and lose your blues. I
first or sec-ond class-es, no dif-f'rence in the fare. If

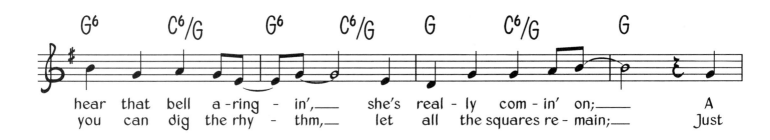

hear that bell a-ring-in', she's real-ly com-in' on; A
you can dig the rhy-thm, let all the squares re-main; Just

rock-in' and a swing-in', latch on be-fore she's gone.
leave your wor-ries with 'em, and take the right-eous train.
Get on board,

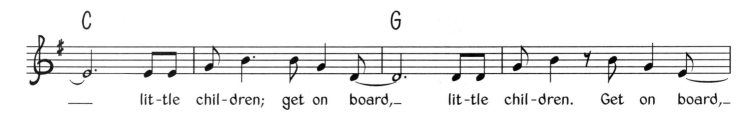

lit-tle chil-dren; get on board, lit-tle chil-dren. Get on board,

lit-tle chil-dren,___ there's lots of room for all.___ Get on board,___

lit-tle chil-dren; get on board,___ lit-tle chil-dren. Get on board,___

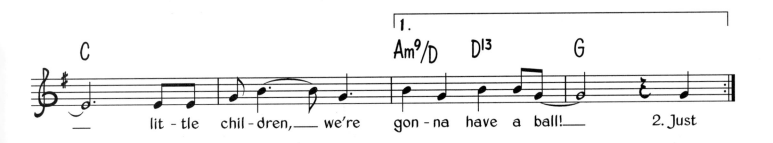

lit-tle chil-dren,___ we're gon-na have a ball!___ 2. Just

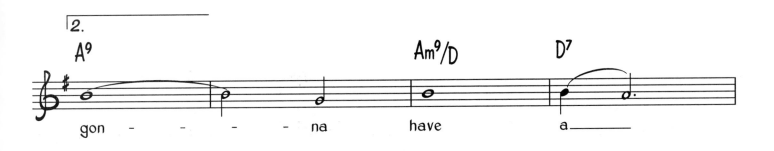

gon - - - na have a___

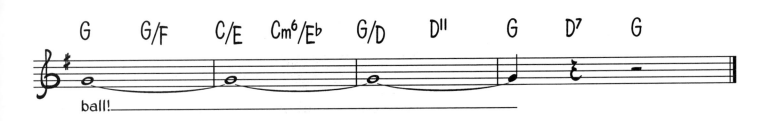

ball!___

Guys And Dolls

Words & Music by Frank Loesser

Medium swing

When you see a guy____ reach for stars in the sky,____ You can
see a dame____ change the shape of her frame,__ You can

bet that he's do - ing it for some doll._____ When you
bet she's re - duc - ing it for some guy._____ When you

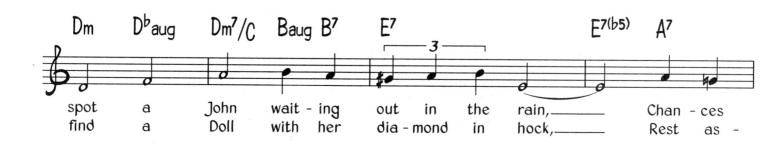

spot a John wait - ing out in the rain,_____ Chan - ces
find a Doll with her dia - mond in hock,_____ Rest as -

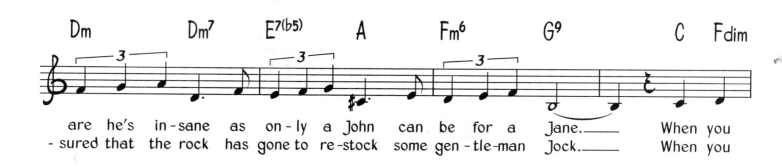

are he's in - sane as on - ly a John can be for a Jane.____ When you
- sured that the rock has gone to re - stock some gen - tle - man Jock.____ When you

meet a gent ___ pay - ing all kinds of rent ___ For a
see a mouse ___ hur - ry out of the house, ___ And she

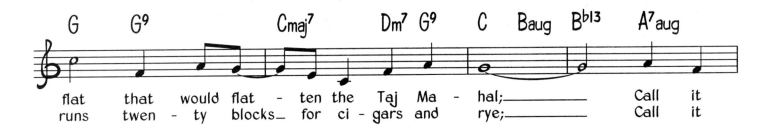

flat that would flat - ten the Taj Ma - hal; ___ Call it
runs twen - ty blocks ___ for ci - gars and rye; ___ Call it

sad, call it fun - ny, but it's bet - ter than ev - en mo -
dumb, call it clev - er, ah, but you can give odds for - ev -

- ney That the guy's on - ly do - ing it for some
- er That the doll's on - ly do - ing it for some

doll. On the oth - er hand: When you

guy. ___

Hallelujah I Love Her So

Words & Music by Ray Charles

Hand Me Down Love

Words & Music by Duke Ellington & Carl Sigman

Don't want your hand-me-down love,___ Don't want your throw-a-way sigh.___
It does-n't come from your heart._

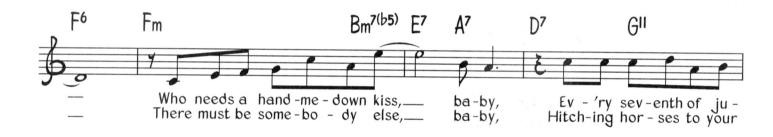

Who needs a hand-me-down kiss,___ ba-by, Ev-'ry sev-enth of ju-
There must be some-bo-dy else,___ ba-by, Hitch-ing hor-ses to your

- ly?   Don't want your hand me-down love,   cart!_____

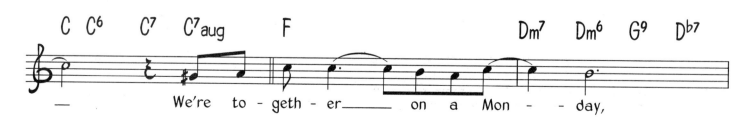

We're to-geth-er___ on a Mon--day,

But what__ a - bout Sun - - day? And Sat - ur - day,

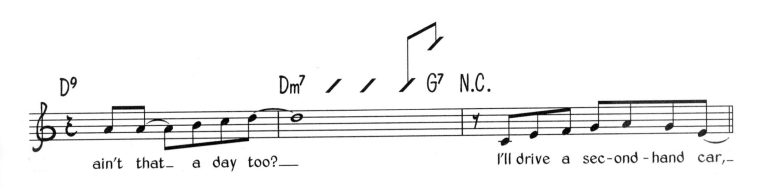

ain't that__ a day too?__ I'll drive a sec - ond - hand car,__

__ I'll wear a hand - me - down glove.__ But what's my heart gon - na do,__

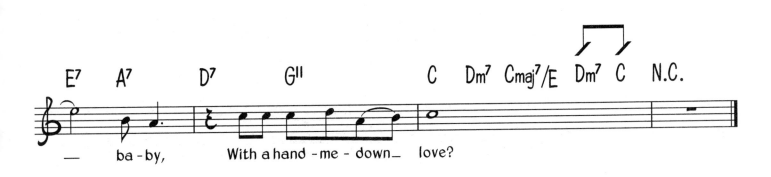

__ ba - by, With a hand - me - down__ love?

Duke Ellington

Heartaches

Words by John Klenner ★ Music by Al Hoffman

Hey! Ba-Ba-Re-Bop

Words & Music by Lionel Hampton & Curley Hammer

Medium fast

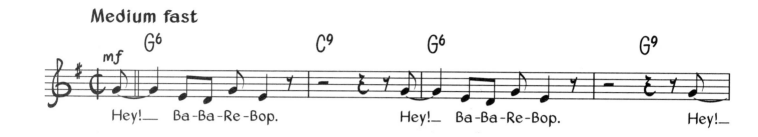

Hey!__ Ba-Ba-Re-Bop.   Hey!__ Ba-Ba-Re-Bop.   Hey!__

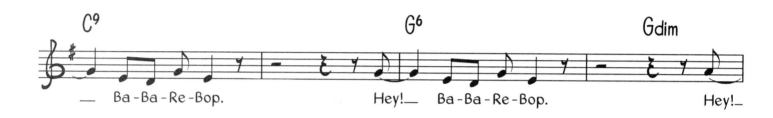

__ Ba-Ba-Re-Bop.   Hey!__ Ba-Ba-Re-Bop.   Hey!__

__ Ba-Ba-Re-Bop.   Yes,__ your ba-by knows.__   Ma-

-til-da Brown__ told Old King Tut,__ "If you can't say Re-Bop, keep your

big mouth shut!"__Sing-in' Hey! Ba-Ba-Re-Bop.   Hey!__ Ba-Ba-Re-Bop.

Hey!__ Ba-Ba - Re-Bop.   Yes,__ your ba-by knows.__

Ma - ma's on the chair, pa - pa's on the cot, Ba - by's in the crib blow - in' his

nat - 'ral top,_ sing - in' Hey!_ Ba - Ba - Re - Bop, Hey!_ Ba - Ba - Re - Bop.

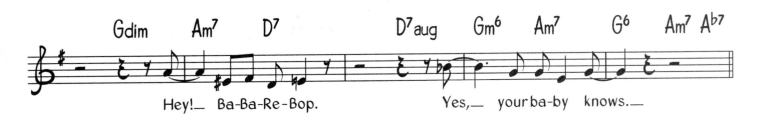

Hey!_ Ba - Ba - Re - Bop. Yes,_ your ba - by knows._

Up on the moun - tain, look - in' at the sea, Look - in' for that cat that stole my

ba - by from me,_ sing - in' Hey! Ba - Ba - Re - Bop, Hey!_ Ba - Ba - Re - Bop.

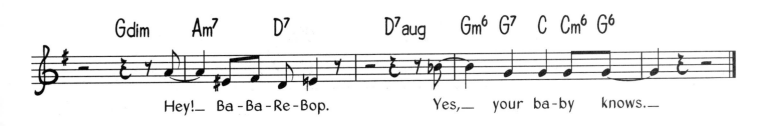

Hey!_ Ba - Ba - Re - Bop. Yes,_ your ba - by knows._

High Society

Words & Music by Walter Melrose & Porter Steele

Hold Me

Words & Music by Little Jack Little, Dave Oppenheim & Ira Schuster

Honeysuckle Rose

Music by Thomas 'Fats' Waller ★ Words by Andy Razaf

97

I Got A Woman

Words & Music by Ray Charles

I Can't Give You Anything But Love

Words by Dorothy Fields ★ Music by Jimmy McHugh

I Should Care

Words & Music by Sammy Cahn, Axel Stordahl & Paul Weston

I'll Remember April

Words & Music by Don Raye, Gene de Paul & Patricia Johnson

Easy swing

This love - ly day will leng - then in - to ev - 'ning,

We'll sigh good - bye to all we've ev - er had.____ A -

- lone where we have walked to - geth - er,_____ I'll re -

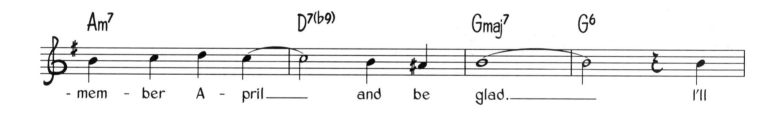

- mem - ber A - pril____ and be glad._____ I'll

be con - tent____ you loved me once in A - pril; Your

lips were warm____ and love and Spring were new.____ But I'm not a -

Am¹¹   D⁷   Gmaj⁷   G⁶

-fraid   of   Au - tumn   and   her   sor - row,_____ For I'll re -

F♯m¹¹   B⁹   3   Emaj⁷ E⁶   Am⁹   D¹³

- mem - ber_____   A - pril   and   you._____

G   G⁶   C⁹

The   fire   will   dwin - dle   in - to   glow - ing   ash - es,

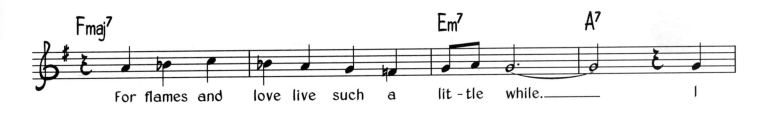

Fmaj⁷   Em⁷   A⁷

For flames and   love live such   a   lit - tle   while._____   I

Am⁷(b5)   D⁷   D/C   3   Bm⁷   E⁹

won't   for - get,_____ but   I won't be   lone - ly;_____   I'll re -

Am⁷   D⁷(b9)   D¹³(b9)   G   Am⁷   A♭maj⁷ G⁶/⁹

- mem - ber   A - pril,_____ and   I'll   smile._____

I'm Gettin' Sentimental Over You

Words by Ned Washington ★ Music by Geo. Bassman

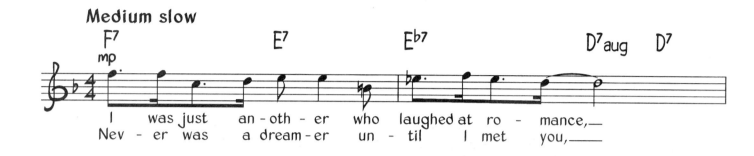

I was just an-oth-er who laughed at ro - mance,___
Nev - er was a dream-er un - til I met you,___

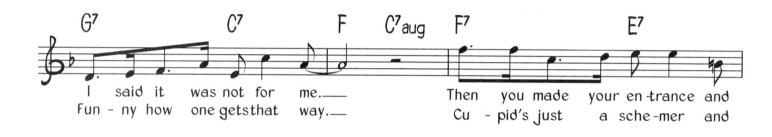

I said it was not for me.___ Then you made your en-trance and
Fun - ny how one gets that way.___ Cu - pid's just a sche-mer and

right at a glance,___ I knew this was meant for me.___
I nev - er knew,___ Now I'm dream-ing dreams all day.___

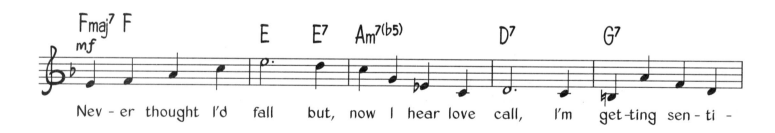

Nev - er thought I'd fall but, now I hear love call, I'm get-ting sen - ti -

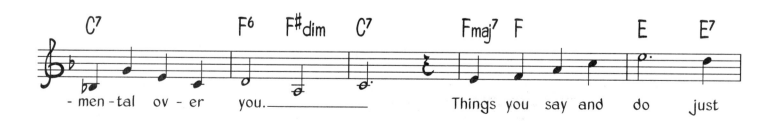

- men-tal ov - er you._____ Things you say and do just

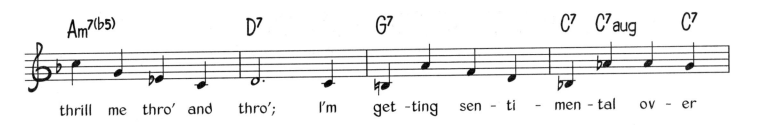

thrill me thro' and thro'; I'm get -ting sen - ti - men -tal ov - er

you._____ I thought I was hap -py, I could live with - out

love; Now I must ad - mit that love is all I'm think -ing

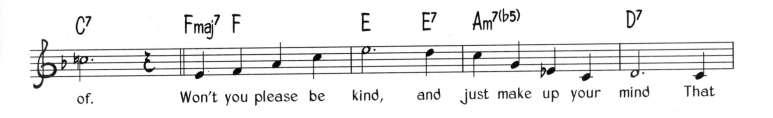

of. Won't you please be kind, and just make up your mind That

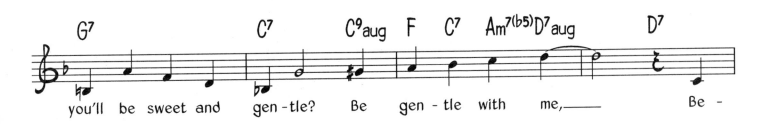

you'll be sweet and gen -tle? Be gen - tle with me,_____ Be -

cause I'm sen - ti - men -tal ov - er you._____

I'm Beginning To See The Light

Words & Music by Harry James, Duke Ellington, Johnny Hodges & Don George

I'm Old Fashioned

Music by Jerome Kern ★ Words by Johnny Mercer

In A Mellow Tone

By Duke Ellington & Milt Gabler

Medium tempo

In a mel - low tone,___ feel - ing fan - cy - free;___

And I'm not a - lone,___ I've got com - pa - ny.___

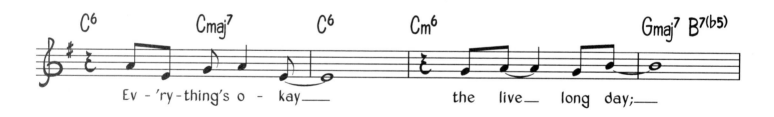

Ev - 'ry-thing's o - kay___ the live___ long day;___

With this mel - low song,___ I can't___ go wrong.___

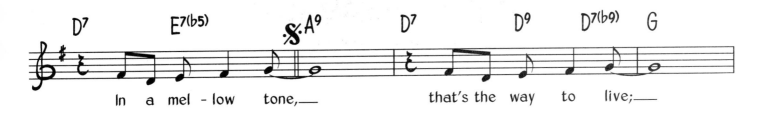

In a mel - low tone, ___ that's the way to live; ___

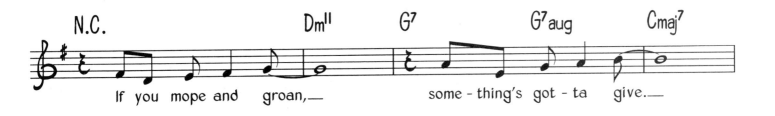

If you mope and groan, ___ some - thing's got - ta give. ___

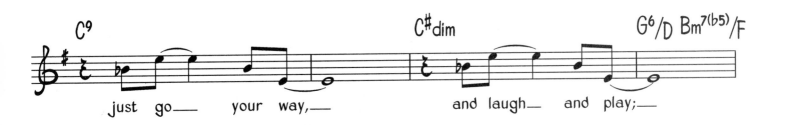

just go ___ your way, ___ and laugh ___ and play; ___

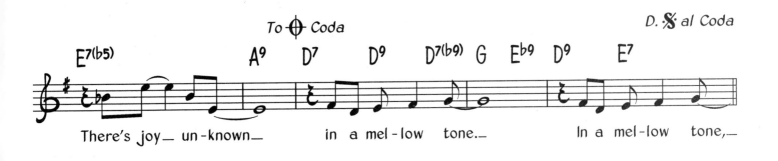

There's joy ___ un - known ___ in a mel - low tone. ___ In a mel - low tone, ___

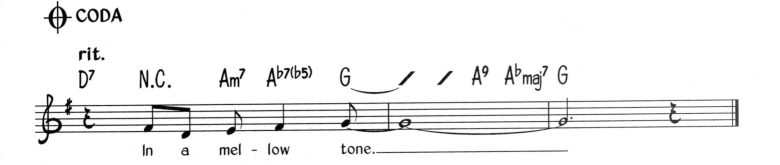

In a mel - low tone. ___

In The Still Of The Night

Words & Music by Cole Porter

"Do_____ you love me as I love

you?_____ Are you my life to be,

my dream come true?"_____ Or will this

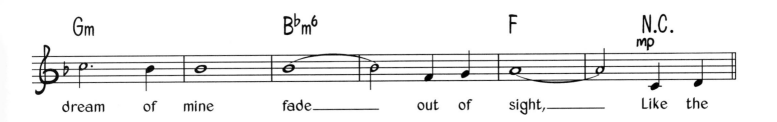

dream of mine fade_____ out of sight,_____ Like the

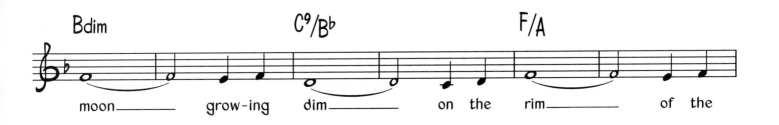

moon_____ grow-ing dim_____ on the rim_____ of the

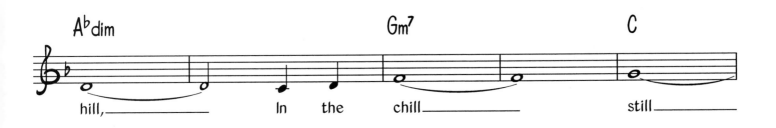

hill,_____ In the chill_____ still_____

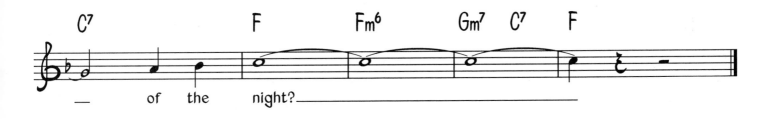

— of the night?_____

In Walked Bud

By Thelonious Monk

In Your Own Sweet Way

Music by Dave Brubeck ★ Words by Iola Brubeck

Is You Is, Or Is You Ain't (Ma' Baby)

Words & Music by Billy Austin & Louis Jordan

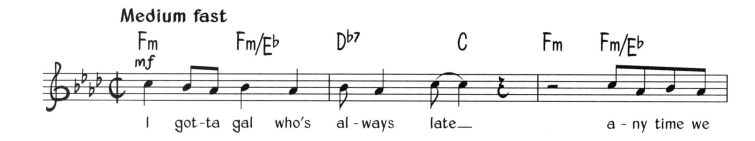

I got-ta gal who's al-ways late— a-ny time we

have a date;— But I love her,———— yes, I love her.————

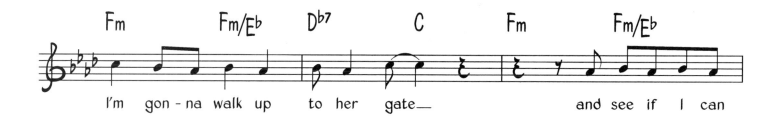

I'm gon-na walk up to her gate— and see if I can

get it straight;— 'Cos I want her.———————— I'm gon-na ask her:————

— Is you is, or is you ain't ma' ba - by?

The way you're act - ing late-ly makes me doubt.—

Intermission Riff

Words by Steve Graham ★ Music by Ray Wetzel

It Don't Mean A Thing (If It Ain't Got That Swing)

Words by Irving Mills ★ Music by Duke Ellington

It Might As Well Be Spring

Words by Oscar Hammerstein II ★ Music by Richard Rodgers

It's A Raggy Waltz

Music by Dave Brubeck

Medium fast jazz waltz

It's Nice To Go Trav'ling

Words by Sammy Cahn ★ Music by James Van Heusen

It Had To Be You

Words by Gus Kahn ★ Music by Isham Jones

J.D.'s Boogie Woogie

by Jimmy Dorsey & Marvin Wright

Ja-Da

Words & Music by Bob Carleton

Medium bounce

Jazz 'N' Samba (So Danco Samba)

Original Words & Music by Antonio Carlos Jobim & Vinicius de Moraes. English Words by Norman Gimbel

Jeepers Creepers

Music by Harry Warren ★ Words by Johnny Mercer

Medium fast

I don't care what the wea-ther man says; When the wea-ther man say's it's

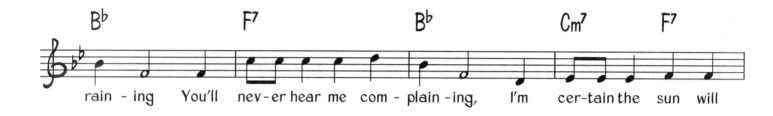

rain - ing You'll nev-er hear me com - plain -ing, I'm cer-tain the sun will

shine. I don't care how the wea-ther vane points; When the wea-ther vane points to

gloom-y, It's got-ta be sun - ny to me When your eyes look in - to

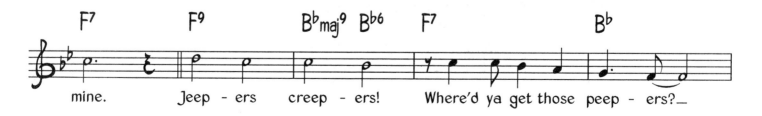

mine. Jeep - ers creep - ers! Where'd ya get those peep - ers?__

Jeep - ers creep - ers! Where'd ya get those eyes? Gosh all

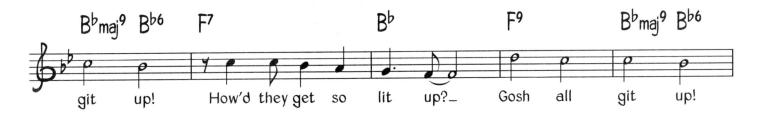

git up! How'd they get so lit up?_ Gosh all git up!

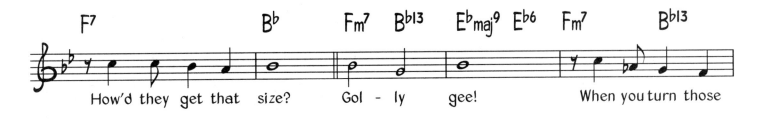

How'd they get that size? Gol - ly gee! When you turn those

heat - ers on,_ Woe is me! Got to put my cheat - ers on._

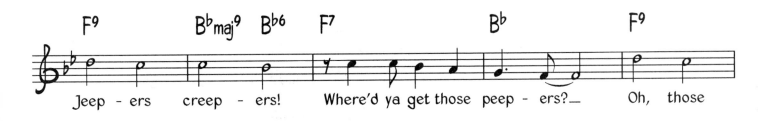

Jeep - ers creep - ers! Where'd ya get those peep - ers?_ Oh, those

weep - ers! How they hyp-no-tize!_ Where'd ya get those eyes?

Just One Of Those Things

Words & Music by Cole Porter

As Do - ro - thy Par - - ker once said_____ to her

boy friend:_ "Fare thee well."_____ As Co - lum - bus an - nounced,

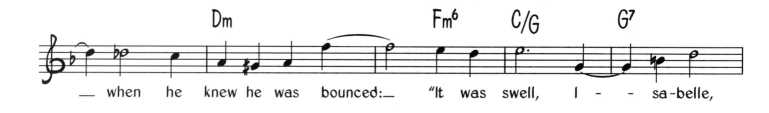

_ when he knew he was bounced:_ "It was swell, I - - sa -belle,

swell"._____ As Ab - el -ard____ said to E - lo - ise:_

_ "Don't for - get____ to drop a line to me, please."_ As

Jul - iet cried___ in her Rom - eo's ear:___ "Rom - eo, why___

___ not face the fact, my dear?"___ It was just one___ of those

things,_____ Just one___ of those cra - zy flings.___

___ One of those bells that now and then rings,

Just one___ of those things.___ It was just one___

___ of those nights,_____ Just one___ of those

fa - bu - lous flights; A trip to the moon on gos - sa - mer

C⁷	F⁶	F♯dim	Fm⁷	B♭⁷

wings,   Just   one ___ of those things,   If   we'd

E♭	B♭9	E♭6

thought a bit___ of the end of it___ when we start - ed paint -

G⁷	C⁶

- ing the town,_____ We'd have been a - ware___ that our

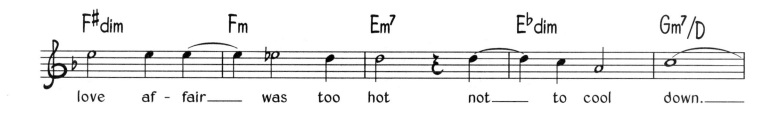

F♯dim	Fm	Em⁷	E♭dim	Gm⁷/D

love af - fair___ was too hot   not___ to cool down.___

C⁷	A⁷	Dm	A/C♯	F⁷/C

_ So good - bye,   dear,_ and A - men;_____ Here's hop -

B♭maj⁷	B♭6	Am⁷	D⁷

- ing we meet now and then.___ It was great fun,___ but it was

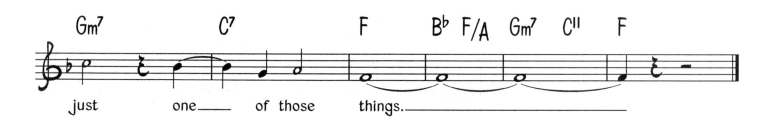

Gm⁷	C⁷	F	B♭	F/A	Gm⁷	C¹¹	F

just   one ___ of those   things._____

Line For Lyons

By Gerry Mulligan

Let's Get Away From It All

Music by Matt Dennis ★ Words by Tom Adair

Medium swing

Let's take a boat to Ber - mu - da,— let's take a plane to Saint Paul;

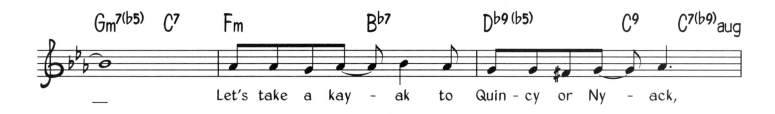

Let's take a kay - ak to Quin - cy or Ny - ack,

Let's get a - way— from it all.— Let's take a trip— in a trail -

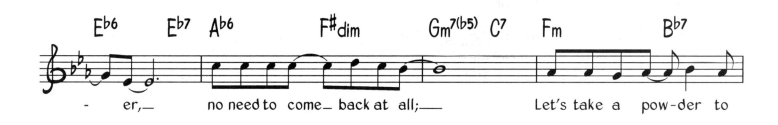

- er,— no need to come— back at all;— Let's take a pow-der to

Bos - ton for chow - der, Let's get a - way— from it all.— We'll

tra - vel 'round from town to town,— we'll vis - it ev - 'ry

state; A - las - ka and Ha - wa - ii, too,— then all the for - ty eight.—

— Let's go a - gain— to Ni - a - - gra;—

this time we'll look— at the Fall.— Let's leave our hut,— dear; get

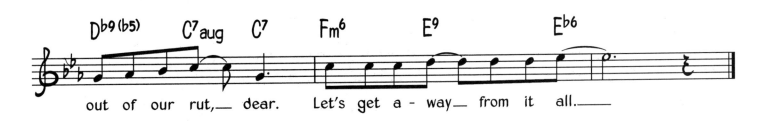

out of our rut,— dear. Let's get a - way— from it all.—

Lover

Music by Richard Rodgers ★ Words by Lorenz Hart

Lullaby Of Birdland

Music by George Shearing ★ Words by George David Weiss

Lul-la-by of Bird-land, that's what I___ Al-ways hear_ when you sigh,__

Nev-er in my word-land could there be ways_ to re-veal,_____ In a phrase,_

— how I feel!__ Have you ev-erheard two tur-tle doves_ Bill and coo_

when they love?__ That's the kind of mag-ic mus-ic we make_ with our lips_

____ when we kiss!__ And there's a weep-y old wil - low,___

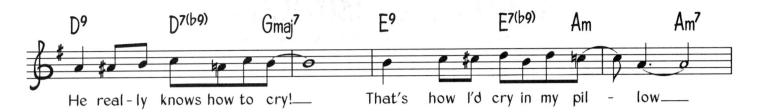

He real-ly knows how to cry!___ That's how I'd cry in my pil - low___

If you should tell me fare - well___ and good-bye!_ Lul - la - by of Bird -land,

whis -per low,___ Kiss me sweet_ and we'll go___ Fly-in' high in bird-land,

high in the sky___ up a - bove,_____ All be - cause_ we're in love!___

___ all be - cause_ we're in love!_____

Luck Be A Lady

Words & Music by Frank Loesser

fair,_____ it is - n't nice._____ A

la - dy does - n't wan - der all ov - er the room And

blow on some oth - er guy's dice!_____ So

let's keep the par - ty po - lite,_____

Nev - er get out of my sight:_____

Stick with me ba - by, I'm the fel - low you came in with.

Luck be a la - dy, Luck be a la - dy,

Luck be a la - dy to - night!_____

Mercy, Mercy, Mercy

Words by Gail Fisher Levy & Vincent Levy ★ Music by Josef Zawinul

Manhattan Spiritual

By Billy Maxted

Miles Ahead

By Miles Davis

Theme From Mission: Impossible

By Lalo Schifrin

Mississippi Mud

Words & Music by Harry Barris

Medium fast swing

When the sun goes down, the tide goes out, The

peo-ple gath-er round, and they all be-gin to shout. Hey! Hey!

Un-cle Dud!__ It's a treat to beat your feet on the Mis-sis-sip-pi mud; It's a

treat to beat your feet on the Mis-sis-sip-pi mud. What a dance__

do they do,__ Lord-y how I'm tell-in' you.__ They don't need no band,__

They keep time by clap-pin' their hands,— Just as hap-py as a cow,

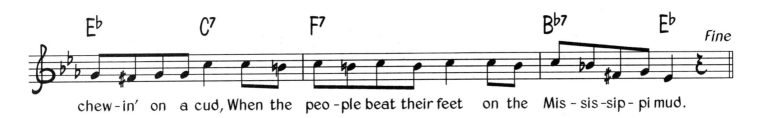

chew-in' on a cud, When the peo-ple beat their feet on the Mis-sis-sip-pi mud.

Interlude

Lord-y how they play it; Good-ness, how they sway it. Un-cle

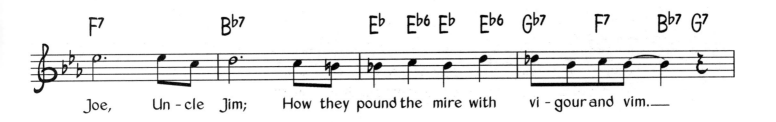

Joe, Un-cle Jim; How they pound the mire with vi-gour and vim.—

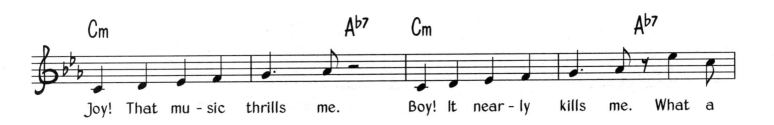

Joy! That mu-sic thrills me. Boy! It near-ly kills me. What a

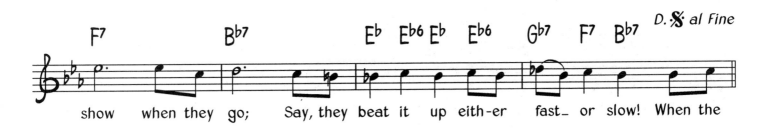

show when they go; Say, they beat it up eith-er fast— or slow! When the

Mobile

Words & Music by Bob Wells & David Holt

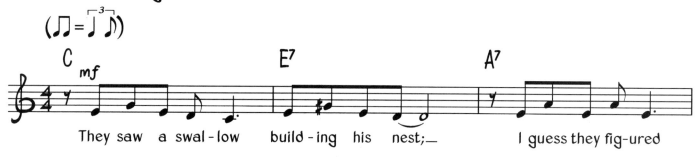

Medium swing

They saw a swal-low build-ing his nest;— I guess they fig-ured he knew best,— So they built a town a-round him and they called it Mo-bile.—

—(Where's that?)— Al-a-ba-ma They took a swamp-land

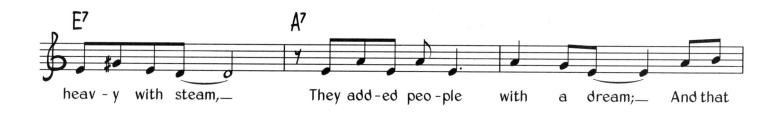

heav-y with steam,— They add-ed peo-ple with a dream;— And that

dream be-came a heav-en by the name of Mo-bile.———

Pret ty soon the town had grown,— till they had a slide trom-bone,—

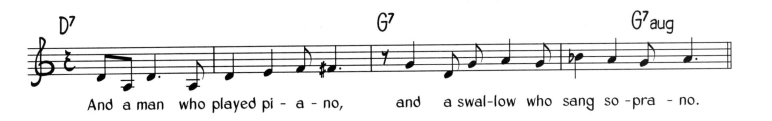

And a man who played pi - a - no, and a swal-low who sang so -pra - no.

No use your wond -'rin' where you should go;— It's on the Gulf of

Mex - i - co,—Where the south-ern belles are ring- in' and the cli -mate's i - deal.—

— It's a hon-ey-suck-le heav- en by the name of Mo -bile.—

Moanin'

Words by Jon Hendricks ★ Music by Bobby Timmons

Moten's Swing

By Buster & Bennie Moten

Mullenium

By Gerry Mulligan

My Blue Heaven

Words by George Whiting ★ Music by Walter Donaldson

My Resistance Is Low

Words by Harold Adamson ★ Music by Hoagy Carmichael

My Very Good Friend The Milkman

Words by Johnny Burke ★ Music by Harold Spina

1. My ve - ry good friend, the milk - man, says That I've been los - ing
   ve - ry good friend, the post - man, says That it would make his

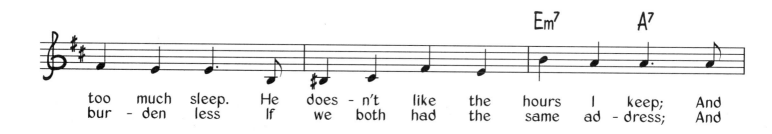

too much sleep. He does - n't like the hours I keep; And
bur - den less If we both had the same ad - dress; And

he sug - gests_ that you should mar - ry me._____
he sug - gests_ that you should mar - ry me._____ 2. My

me._____ Then there's a ve - ry friend - ly fel - low who prints

All the lat-est real es-tate news;___ And ev-'ry day he sends me

blue prints Of cot-tag-es with coun-try views._____ My

ve-ry good friends and neigh-bours say That they've been watch - ing

things I do; And they be - lieve that I love you. So

I sug-gest___ that you should mar - ry me._____

Nice 'N' Easy

Words by Marilyn & Alan Bergman ★ Music by Lew Spence

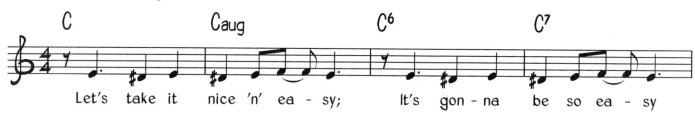

Let's take it nice 'n' ea-sy; It's gon-na be so ea-sy

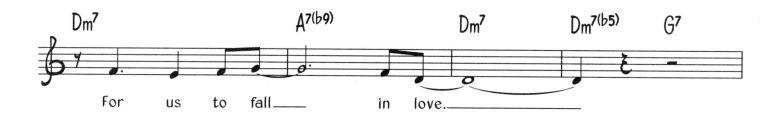

For us to fall___ in love.___

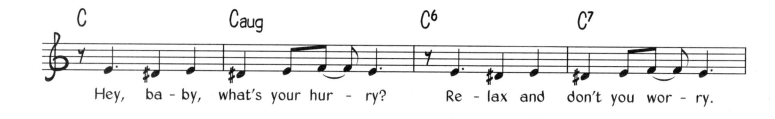

Hey, ba-by, what's your hur-ry? Re-lax and don't you wor-ry.

We're gon-na fall___ in love.___

We're on the road to ro-mance, that's safe to say;___ But let's make

all   the stops   a - long   the way._____

The pro-blem now, of course,__ is   To sim - ply hold your hor - ses;

To   rush would   be   a____ crime._____   'Cos

nice 'n' ea - sy does it;   Nice 'n' ea - sy does it.

Nice 'n' ea - sy does it ev - er - y time._____

Nice Work If You Can Get It

Music & Lyrics by George Gershwin & Ira Gershwin

Night Flight

By R. Bryant

Nine Twenty Special

Words by Bill Engvick ★ Music by Earl Warren

Oh Look At Me Now

Words by John DeVries ★ Music by Joe Bushkin

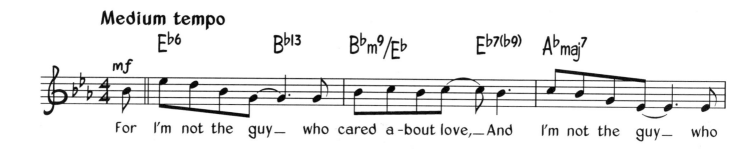

For I'm not the guy— who cared a-bout love,— And I'm not the guy— who

cared a-bout for - tunes and such;— Nev-er cared much,— but look at me

now._____ I nev-er knew— the tech-nique of kiss - in',

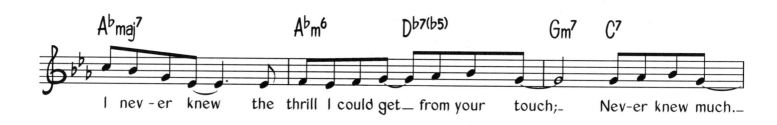

I nev-er knew the thrill I could get— from your touch;— Nev-er knew much.—

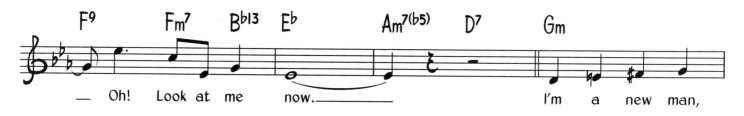

— Oh! Look at me now._____ I'm a new man,

better than— Ca-sa-no-va at his best.— With a new heart,

brand new start,— I'm so proud I'm bust-in' my vest.— So

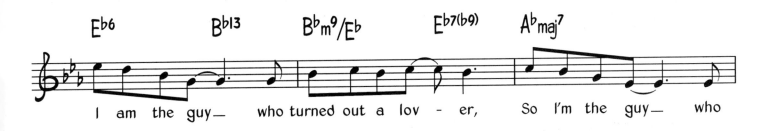

I am the guy— who turned out a lov - er, So I'm the guy— who

laughed at those blue— dia-mond rings;— One of those things.— Oh! Look at me

now.————— now.—————

O Barquinho (Little Boat)

Music by Roberto Menescal ★ Original Words by Ronaldo Boscoli ★ English Lyric by Buddy Kaye

Oh, Lady, Be Good

Music & Lyrics by George Gershwin & Ira Gershwin

Ol' Man Mose

By Louis Armstrong & Zilner Trenton Randolph

On The Sunny Side Of The Street

Words by Dorothy Fields ★ Music by Jimmy McHugh

One Note Samba (Samba De Uma Nota So)

Original Words by N. Mendonca ★ English Lyric by Jon Hendricks ★ Music by Antonio Carlos Jobim

Bossa nova

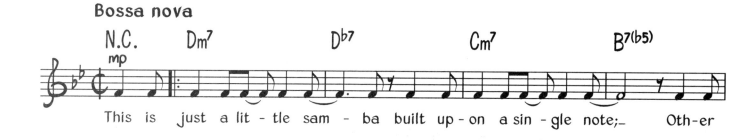

This is just a lit - tle sam - ba built up-on a sin - gle note;_ Oth-er

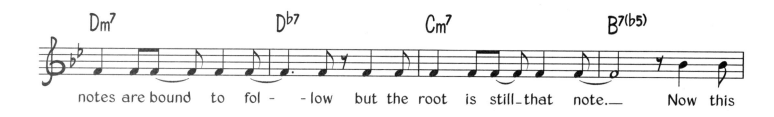

notes are bound to fol - -low but the root is still_that note._ Now this

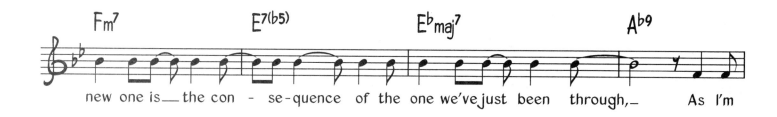

new one is_the con - se-quence of the one we've just been through,_ As I'm

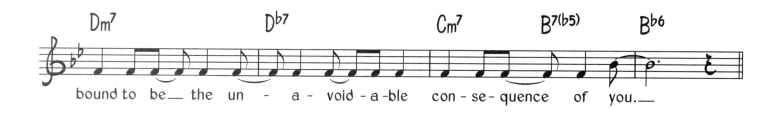

bound to be_ the un - a - void - a -ble con - se - quence of you._

There's so ma-ny peo-ple who can talk and talk and talk and just say noth-ing, or near-ly

noth - ing.— I have used up all the scale I know and at the end I've come to

noth -ing, or near-ly noth -ing. So I come back to— my first— note, as I

must come back— to you.— I will pour in-to—that one— note all the

love I feel— for you.— A - ny -one who wants— the whole— show: Re, Mi,

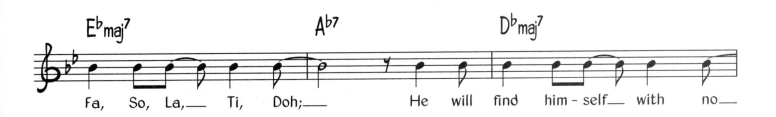

Fa, So, La,— Ti, Doh;— He will find him - self— with no—

_ show. Bet -ter play— the note— you know.— This is —

Opus One

Words & Music by Sy Oliver

The Orange Blossom Special

Words & Music by Ervin T. Rouse

Fast

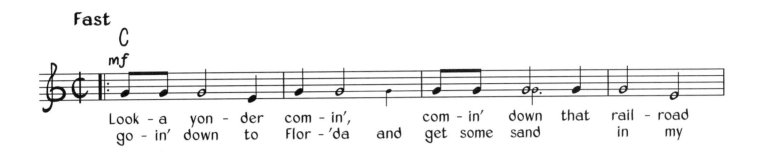

Look - a yon - der com - in', com - in' down that rail - road
go - in' down to Flor - 'da and get some sand in my

track!_____ Hey, look - a yon - der com - in',
shoes;_____ Or may - be Ca - li - for - nia and

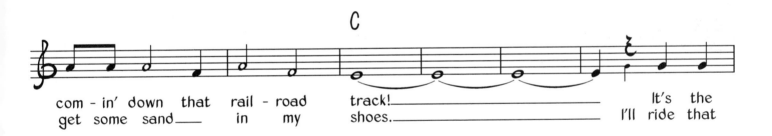

com - in' down that rail - road track!_____ It's the
get some sand___ in my shoes._____ I'll ride that

O - range Blos - som Spe - cial, bring - in' my ba - - by
O - range Blos - som Spe - cial and lose these New___ York

1. 2.

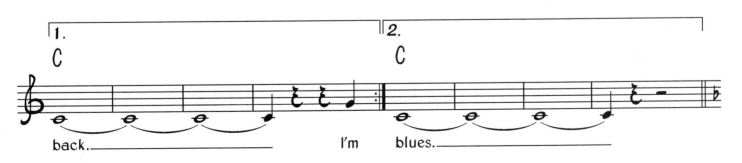

back._____ I'm blues._____

(Instrumental)

Talk a-bout a - trav - 'lin', she's the fast-est train on the

line._____ Talk a-bout a - trav-'lin', she's the

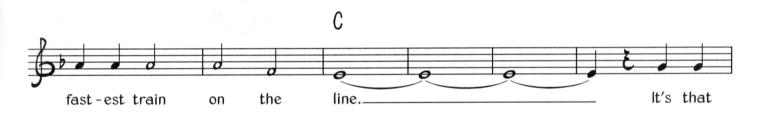

fast-est train on the line._____ It's that

O - range Blos-som Spe - cial, roll - in' down the Sea - board

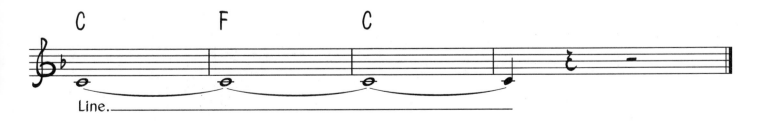

Line._____

Orange Coloured Sky

Words & Music by Milton DeLugg & Willie Stein

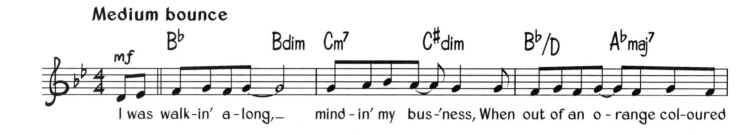

I was walk-in' a-long,— mind-in' my bus-'ness, When out of an o-range col-oured

sky: Flash! Bam! A-la-ka-zam!— Won-der-ful you— came

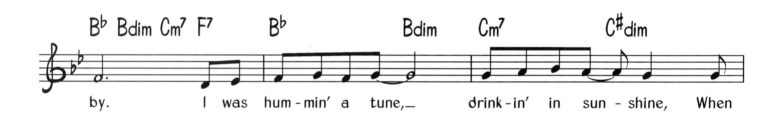

by. I was hum-min' a tune,— drink-in' in sun-shine, When

out of that o-range col-oured view: Flash! Bam! A-la-ka-zam!—

I got a look— at you. One look and I yelled "Tim-ber,

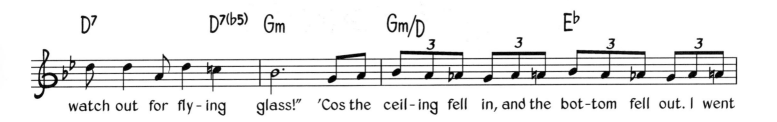

watch out for fly-ing glass!" 'Cos the ceil-ing fell in, and the bot-tom fell out. I went

in-to a spin, and I start-ed to shout "I've been hit! This is it! This is it!" I was

walk-in' a - long,— mind-in' my bus-'ness, When love came and hit— me in the

eye. Flash! Bam! A - la - ka - zam!— Out of an o-range co-loured,

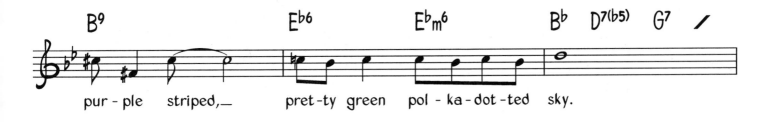

pur - ple striped,— pret-ty green pol - ka - dot - ted sky.

Flash! Bam! A - la - ka - zam!— and good - bye._____

Organ Grinder's Swing

Words by Mitchell Parish & Irving Mills ★ Music by Will Hudson

Medium fast bounce

Who's that com-ing down the street?— Good old or-gan grind-er Pete.—

He's the lat-est rhy-thm king,— with his or-gan grind-er's swing.— Da-dya,—

Pa— swings it,— so does Ma;— Ma— swings it,— so does Pa.—
Da-dya.— Da-dya,—

You— swing it,— so do I;— I— swing it,— so do you.—
Da-dya.—

When he turns that han-dle down,— mu-sic goes a -round and 'round;—

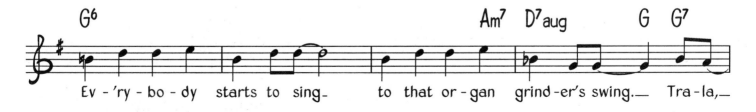

Ev -'ry-bo-dy starts to sing— to that or-gan grind-er's swing.— Tra-la,—

Pa— swings it,— so does Ma; Ma— swings it,— so does Pa.—
Tra - la.————————— Tra - la,—

You— swing it,— so do I; I— swing it,— so do you.—
Tra - la.—————————

All the chil-dren tag a-long,— just to lis-ten to his song;—

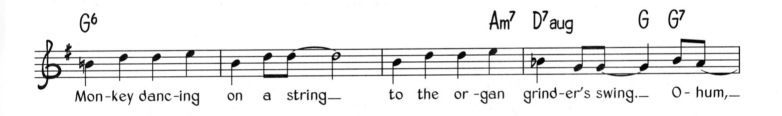

Mon-key danc-ing on a string— to the or-gan grind-er's swing.— O-hum,—

Pa— swings it,— so does Ma; Ma— swings it,— so does Pa.—
O - hum.————————— O-hum,—

You— swing it,— so do I; I— swing it,— so do you.—
O - hum.—————————

Ornithology

By Charlie Parker & Benny Harris

Medium swing

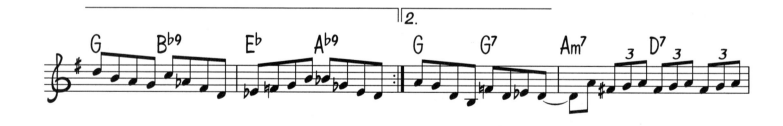

Out Of Nowhere

Music by John Green ★ Lyrics by Edward Heyman

Pennies From Heaven

Words by John Burke ★ Music by Arthur Johnston

Pent Up House

By Sonny Rollins

Medium fast

Count Basie

Perdido

Music by Juan Tizol ★ Words by Harry Lenk and Ervin Drake

Petite Fleur (Little Flower)

Words & Music by Sidney Bechet

Pick Yourself Up

Music by Jerome Kern ★ Words by Dorothy Fields

Noth-ing's im-pos-si-ble, I have found; For, when my chin is on the ground, I

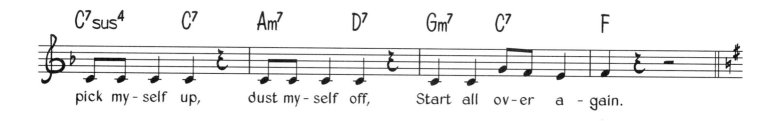

pick my-self up, dust my-self off, Start all ov-er a-gain.

Don't lose your con-fi-dence if you slip; Be grate-ful for a pleas-ant trip, And

pick your-self up, dust your-self off, Start all ov-er a-gain.

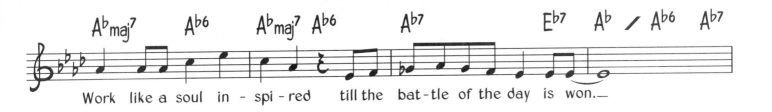

Work like a soul in - spi - red till the bat - tle of the day is won.—

You may be sick and ti - red; but you'll be a man, my son!

Do you re - mem - ber the fa - mous men Who had to fall to rise a - gain? So

take a deep breath, (Instr.) Pick your - self up, (Instr.)

Dust your - self off, (Instr.) Start all ov - er a - gain

Plymouth Sound

By L. Jack Seymour

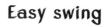

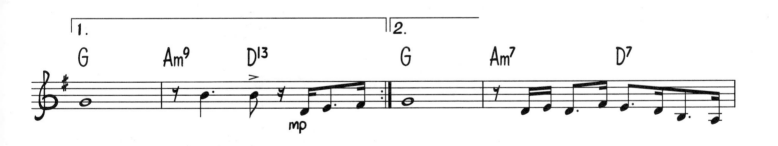

Rhumboogie

Words & Music by Don Raye & Hughie Prince

Medium boogie

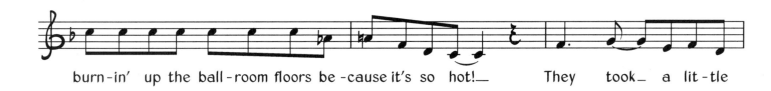

All Har-lem's got a brand new rhy-thm, And it's

burn-in' up the ball-room floors be-cause it's so hot!— They took— a lit-tle

rhum-ba rhy-thm; Then they ad-ded boo-gie woo-gie, and now

look what they've got:— Rhum-boo-gie,_____ Rhum-boo-gie woo-gie;

— It's Har-lem's new cre-a-tion with a Cu-ban syn-co-pa-tion, It's ex-

-ci-ting!_____ Rhum-boo-gie,_____ Rhum-boo-gie woo-gie;

Its cra - zy rhy - thm haunts you; it's bar - ba - ric and it taunts you, It's ex -

- ci - ting!_____ Just plant your both feet on each side,

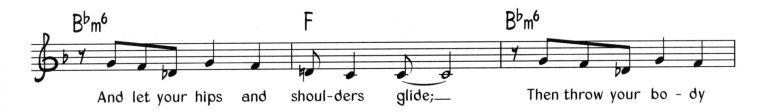

And let your hips and shoul - ders glide;___ Then throw your bo - dy

back and ride.___ (Instrumental) There's no - thin' like Rhum - boo - gie,___

___ Rhum - boo - gie woo - gie;_____ In Har - lem or Ha - va - na, in Pough-

1.

2.

- keep - sie or Sa - van - nah, It's ex - ci - ting!___ Rhum - - ci - ting!___

___ ___ Rhum - boo - gie,___ Rhum - boo - gie!___

Robbin's Nest

By Sir Charles Thompson & Illinois Jacquet

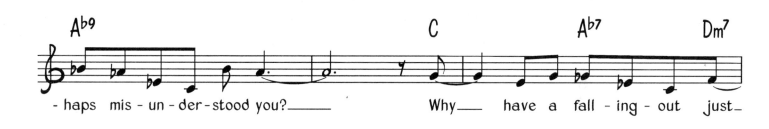

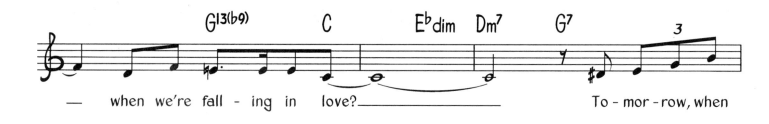

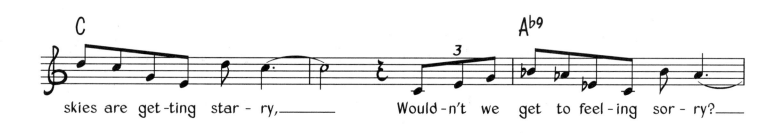

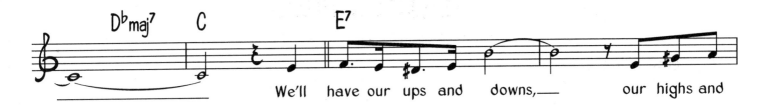

We'll have our ups and downs,___ our highs and

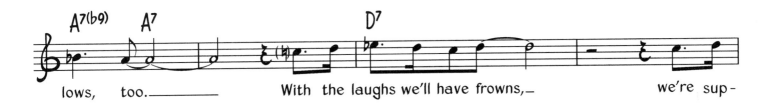

lows, too.___ With the laughs we'll have frowns,___ we're sup-

- posed to.___ We've got-ten a - long so ve -ry nice-ly,___

___ Ba - by, and that's my point pre -cise - ly:___ Why_

___ have a fall -ing out just___ when we're fall -ing in love?___

Raincheck

By Billy Strayhorn

Roundhouse

By Gerry Mulligan

Ruby, My Dear

By Thelonious Monk

Salt Peanuts

Words & Music by John 'Dizzy' Gillespie & Kenny Clarke

Saturday Night Fish Fry

Words & Music by Louis Jordan & Ellis Walsh

Medium fast bounce

Now if you've ev-er been down to New Or-leans,— Then you can

un-der-stand— just what I mean.— Now all thro' the week it's

quiet as a mouse, But on Sa-tur-day night they go from house to house. You

don't have to pay the us-ual ad-mis-sion If you're a cook or a wai-ter or a

good mu-si-cian; So, if you hap-pen to be just pass-in' by,—

Stop in at the Sa-tur-day night fish fry.__ It was rock-in',

It was rock-in'; You ne-ver see such scuf-flin' and

sho-vin' 'til the break of day.__ It was rock-in',

It was rock-in'; You ne-ver see such scuf-flin' and

sho-vin' till the break of day.__ Now if you've __

Satin Doll

Words by Johnny Mercer ★ Music by Duke Ellington & Billy Strayhorn

Save It Pretty Mama

Words & Music by Donald Redman, Joe Davis & Paul Denniker

Save it, pret - ty ma - ma, just for me;__ Re - serve your

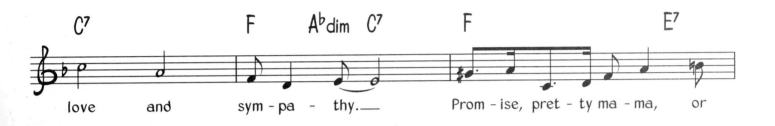

love and sym - pa - thy.__ Prom - ise, pret - ty ma - ma, or

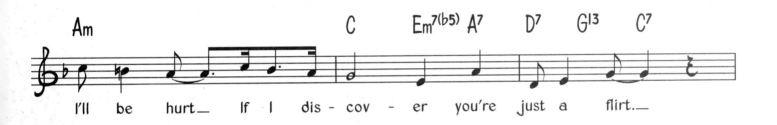

I'll be hurt__ If I dis - cov - er you're just a flirt.__

Ho - ney, my af - fec - tion is tried and true,_ So let me feel the

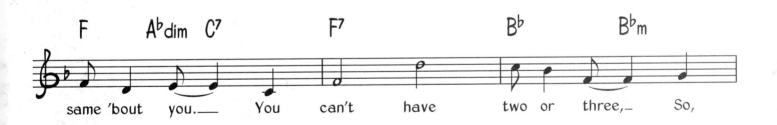

same 'bout you.__ You can't have two or three,_ So,

save it, pret - ty ma - ma, save your love for me.__

Scrub Me Mama (With A Boogie Beat)

Words & Music by Don Raye

Medium Boogie Woogie

In Har-lem there's a lit-tle place where ev-'ry-one goes___ To

see the way a wash-er wo-man wash-es her clothes.___ If you like boo-gie woo-gie rhy-thm

she's got a beat;___ Let the boo-gie woo-gie wash-er wo-man give you a treat!___ On

ev-'ry af-ter-noon at one the ses-sions be-gin,___ And all the boys from all the bands come

down and sit in;___ They sit a-round and knock each oth-er out when they play,___ While the

boo-gie woo-gie wash-er wo-man wash-es all day.___ Rub-did-dle-ub-dub,___

That's just the way she rubs; Rub-did-dle-ub-dub,___ That's just the way she scrubs.

Rub-did-dle-ub-dub,— She wears out all her tubs; She rubs and rubs her knuck-les right on

down to the nubs.— Rub-did-dle-ub-dub,— That's how she kicks it off;

Rub-did-dle-ub-dub,— She keeps it nice and soft. Rub-did-dle-ub-dub,—

till some-one hol-lers "Aw, scrub me, ma-ma, with a boo-gie beat!"— You

rea-ly ought to vis-it there if you've ne-ver been;— It does-n't cost a pen-ny, just come

down and walk in.— If you like boo-gie woo-gie rhy-thm

you'll get a treat;— Let the boo-gie woo-gie wash-er wo-man give you the beat.—

Scrapple From The Apple

By Charlie Parker

Seven Come Eleven

By Benny Goodman & Charlie Christian

Shawnuff

By Charlie Parker & John 'Dizzy' Gillespie

Slightly Out Of Tune (Desafinado)

English Lyric by Jon Hendricks & Jessie Cavanaugh ★ Music by Antonio Carlos Jobim

So Nice

Music & Original Lyrics by Marcos Valle & Paulo Sergio Valle ★ English Lyrics by Norman Gimbel

Some-one to hold me tight, that would be ve - ry nice; Some-one to love me right,

that would be ve - ry nice; Some-one to un-der-stand each lit -tle dream_ in me;

Some - one to take my hand, to be a team_ with me; So nice,_____

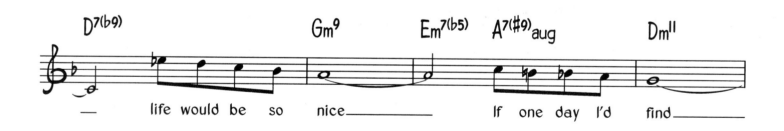

_ life would be so nice_____ If one day I'd find_____

_ some-one who would take my hand and sam-ba thro' life__ with me.

F

Bm⁷

Some-one to cling to me, stay with me right_ or wrong; Some-one to sing to me

E⁷

B♭maj⁷

B♭⁶

some lit-tle sam - ba song; Some-one to take my heart, then give his heart_ to me;

E♭⁹

Am⁷

Some - one who's read-y to give love a start_ with me; Oh, yes,____

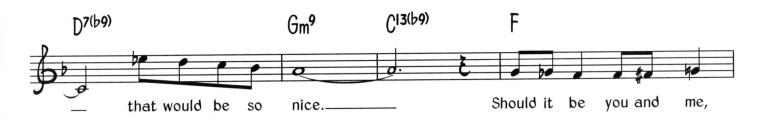

D⁷⁽ᵇ⁹⁾

Gm⁹

C¹³⁽ᵇ⁹⁾

F

_ that would be so nice.____ Should it be you and me,

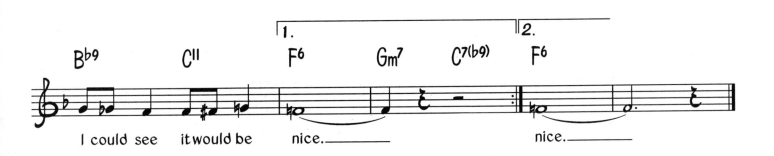

B♭⁹

C¹¹

1.

F⁶

Gm⁷

C⁷⁽ᵇ⁹⁾

2.

F⁶

I could see it would be nice.____ nice.____

Somebody Loves Me

Music & Lyrics by George Gershwin, Ballard MacDonald & B.G. DeSylva

Medium swing

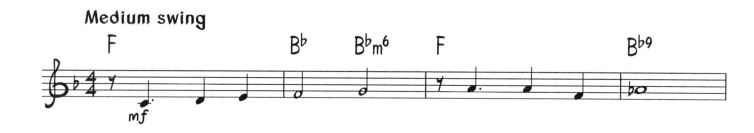

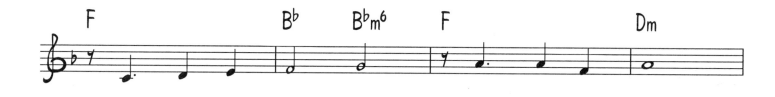

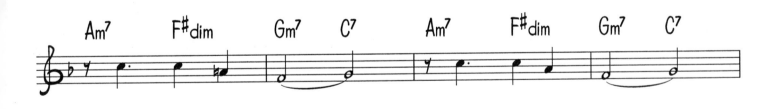

Snootie Little Cutie

Words & Music by Bob Troup

Someday (You'll Be Sorry)

Words & Music by Louis Armstrong

Splanky

By Neal Hefti

Stay On The Right Side, Sister

Music by Rube Bloom ★ Words by Ted Koehler

Stomp, Look And Listen

By Duke Ellington

Stonewall

By Milt Jackson

Medium fast

D. %: al Coda

⊕ CODA

Stompin' At The Savoy

Words by Andy Razaf ★ Music by Benny Goodman, Edgar Sampson & Chick Webb

Straight No Chaser

By Thelonious Monk

Medium bounce

Struttin' With Some Barbecue

Words by Don Raye ★ Music by Louis Armstrong

Medium swing

Strut -tin' with some bar - be - cue,_____ swing - in' with the band,

Like the hap - py peo - ple do_____ way down in dix -ie - land.

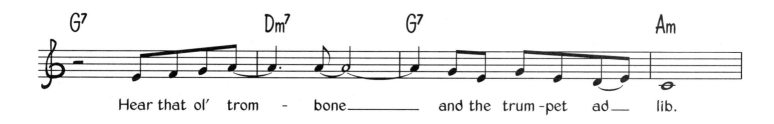

Hear that ol' trom - bone_____ and the trum -pet ad__ lib.

Love__ to hear the lick while I do my pick - in',_____

Pick - in' on a juic - y rib. 'Cos I'm strut -tin' with some bar - be - cue,____

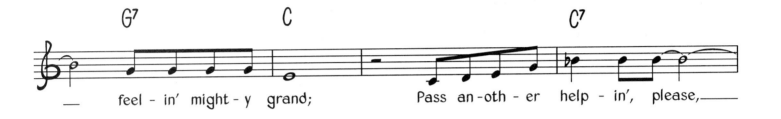

____ feel - in' might - y grand; Pass an - oth - er help - in', please,____

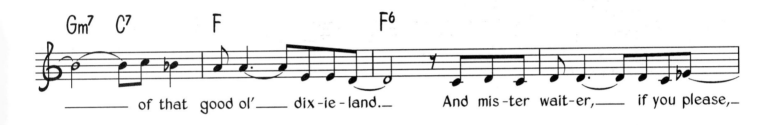

_____ of that good ol'____ dix -ie - land.__ And mis - ter wait - er,____ if you please,—

_____ an - oth - er rib or two;_____ And I'll go strut, strut, strut - tin', strut -

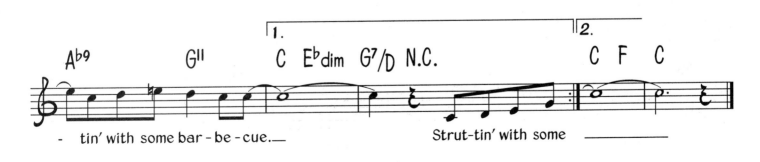

- tin' with some bar - be - cue.__ Strut - tin' with some ____

Stuffy

By Coleman Hawkins

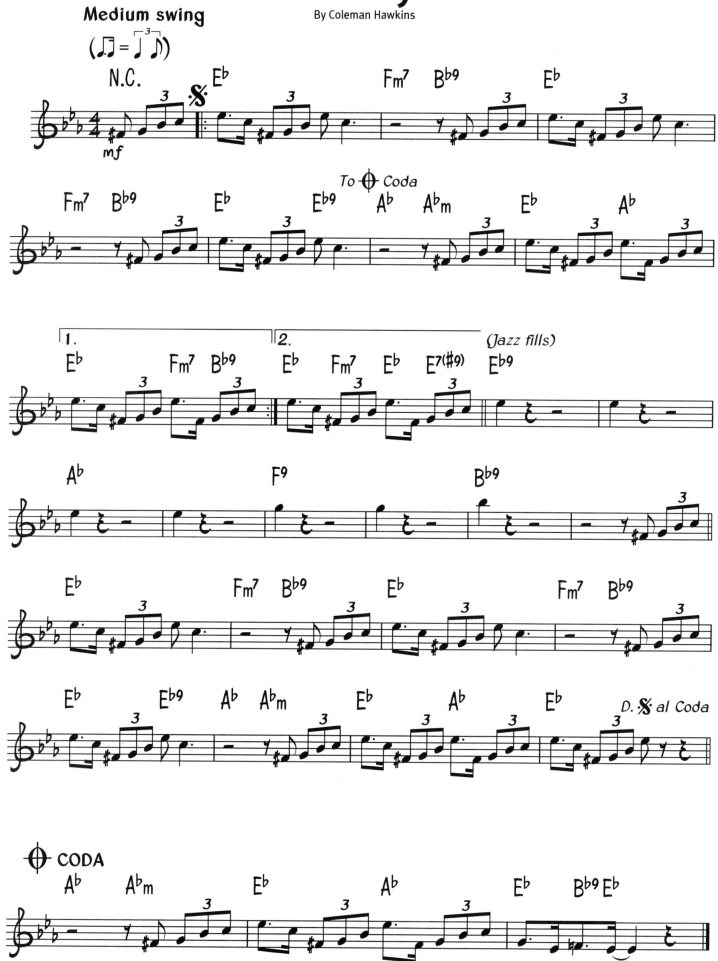

Sultry Serenade

By Duke Ellington

Sweet Sue - Just You

Words by Will J. Harris ★ Music by Victor Young

Ev - 'ry star a - bove_ knows the one I love;_ Sweet Sue,_ just you._ And the moon up high_ knows the rea - son why:_ Sweet Sue,_ it's you._ No one else, it seems,_ ev - er shares my dreams, _ And with - out you, dear, I don't know what I'd do._ In this heart of mine_ you live all the time,_ sweet Sue,_ just you._ Ev - 'ry you._

Take The 'A' Train

Words & Music by Billy Strayhorn

T'aint What You Do (It's The Way That Cha Do It)

Words & Music by Sy Oliver & James Young

Medium fast

Tain't what you do, it's the way that-cha do it; Tain't what you do, it's the
Tain't what you do, it's the way that-cha do it; Tain't what you say, it's the

way that-cha do it; Tain't what you do, it's the way that-cha do it;
way that-cha say it; Tain't what you say, it's the way that-cha say it;

that's what gets_ re-sults._ Tain't what you do, it's the
that's what gets_ re-sults._ Tain't what you croon, it's the

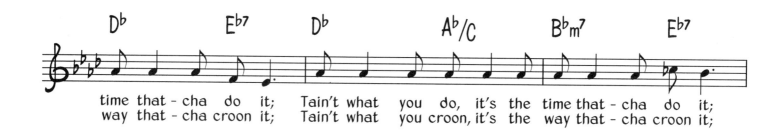

time that-cha do it; Tain't what you do, it's the time that-cha do it;
way that-cha croon it; Tain't what you croon, it's the way that-cha croon it;

Tain't what you do, it's the time that-cha do it; that's what gets_ re-sults._
Tain't what you croon, it's the way that-cha croon it; that's what gets_ re-sults._

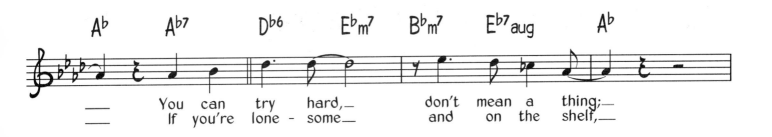

Ab   Ab7   Db6   Ebm7   Bbm7   Eb7aug   Ab

You can try hard,— don't mean a thing;—
If you're lone - some— and on the shelf,—

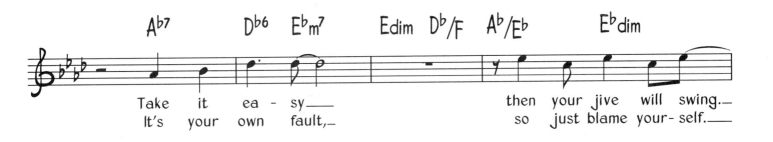

Ab7   Db6   Ebm7   Edim   Db/F   Ab/Eb   Ebdim

Take it ea - sy— then your jive will swing.—
It's your own fault,— so just blame your- self.—

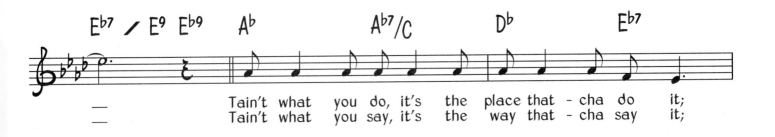

Eb7 ╱ E9 Eb9   Ab   Ab7/C   Db   Eb7

Tain't what you do, it's the place that - cha do it;
Tain't what you say, it's the way that - cha say it;

Db   Ab/C   Bbm7   Eb7   Ab   Ab7/C

Tain't what you do, it's the time that - cha do it; Tain't what you do, it's the
Tain't what you croon, it's the way that - cha croon it; Tain't what you do, it's the

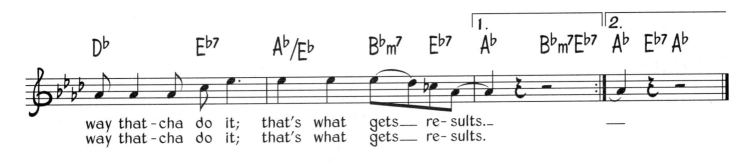

Db   Eb7   Ab/Eb   Bbm7 Eb7   [1.] Ab   Bbm7Eb7 [2.] Ab   Eb7 Ab

way that - cha do it; that's what gets— re- sults.—
way that - cha do it; that's what gets— re- sults.

Take Five

By Paul Desmond

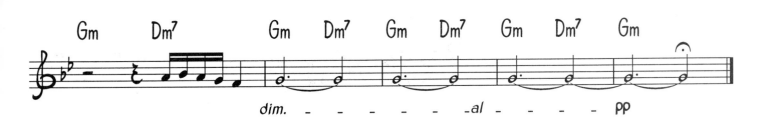

dim. _ _ _ _ _ _al _ _ _ pp

237

Tangerine

Music by Victor Schertzinger ★ Words by Johnny Mercer

Tel Aviv

By Herbie Mann

That Old Black Magic

Music by Harold Arlen ★ Words by Johnny Mercer

Medium fast

Db

And then that__ el -- e - va - tor starts it's__ ride;__

Db7   Ab6   Abm6   Ebmaj9

And down and__ down__ I go, Round and__ round__

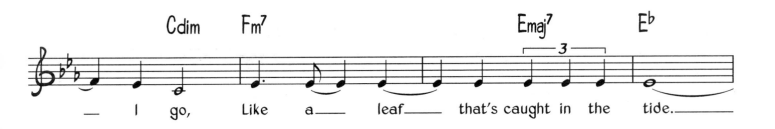

Cdim   Fm7   Emaj7   Eb

__ I go, Like a__ leaf__ that's caught in the tide.__

N.C.   Cm   3   Ab9(#11)

__ I should stay a - way__ but what can I do?__

        G9   C13

__ I hear your name,__ and I'm a - flame;__

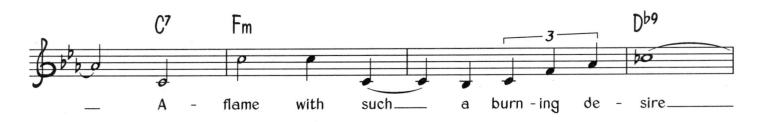

C7   Fm   3   Db9

__ A - flame with such__ a burn - ing de - sire__

That on - ly your kiss_____ can put out the fire.____

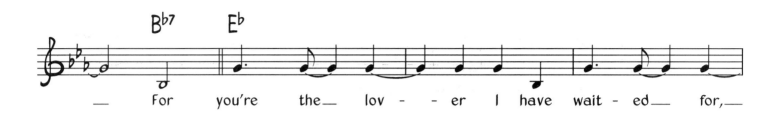

For you're the_ lov - - er I have wait - ed_ for,_

The mate that_ fate_____ had me cre - at - ed_ for;

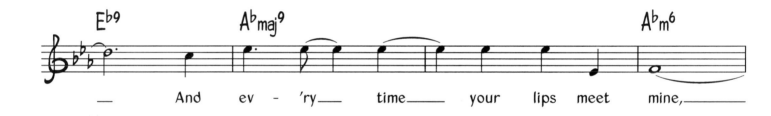

And ev - 'ry_ time_____ your lips meet mine,____

Dar - ling, down and_ down_ I go, Round and_ round_

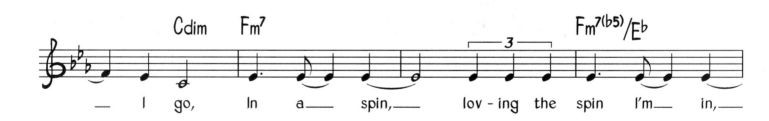

I go, In a_ spin,_ lov - ing the spin I'm_ in,_

Un - der that old black mag - ic called love!____

That's A Plenty

Words by Ray Gilbert ★ Music by Lew Pollack

Medium fast

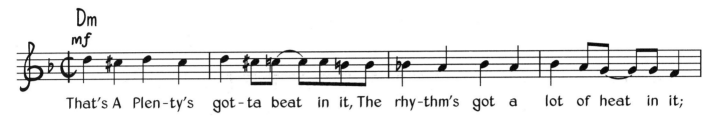

That's A Plen-ty's got-ta beat in it, The rhy-thm's got a lot of heat in it;

Bet-cha five,— ten to five,— It's gon-na get-cha do-in' what it's do-in' to me.— The

Dix-ie-land comes ooz-in' out— of it, The Dix-ie-land-ers sure are proud— of it. They

call it jazz;— what it has,— That's a plen-ty for me.— It takes you down to

New Or-leans, Down Bas-in Street with all the queens.— You don't have to

have the means;— A lit-tle bit of rhy-thm and you're go-in' right with— 'em.

Shut my big brown roll-ing eyes— If you don't rock-et to the skies.—

Hey, boy!— Say, boy!— That's a plen-ty for me.— You're

gon-na get mel-low when that fel-low blows his horn.— Down where the

blues were born,— you'll be gone.— The trum-pets are trump-in', go

do me sump-in'. Beat it out, bro-ther, there's no oth-er re-me-dy.—

C7   F7   B♭

___ And that's a   plen - - ty;___   plen - ty, plen-ty for me.___

A7   Dm

(Instrumental)   Once you start you're gon - na stay_ in it,

A7

Ev -'ry night you're out ca-fe - in' it. Swing your queen;_ what I mean,

Dm   A7   Dm

Bro -ther, you're as gone as an - y   hu - man can be._ And when you're in the mood there

ain't   no stop - pin' it;   Live it, breathe it,   blow your top__ in it;

A7   Dm

That is jazz;_ what it has,_ That's a plen-ty for me.

The Duke

Music by Dave Brubeck ★ Words by Iola Brubeck

Medium tempo

We miss you, Duke,___ we miss you so;___
You wailed, ba - by,___ you wailed a storm;___

We miss your smile that set our hearts a - glow.___ We miss your suave and
Af - ter he made you, God just broke the form.___ You are a man be -

gra - cious ways;___ We loved you mad - ly all your days.___
- yond com - pare;___ So, af - ter you, all men seem square.___

You had such a lyr - ic line,___ And a style words
When you sent us we stayed gone;___ Peo - ple asked us

can't de - fine;___ Your soul - ful phra - ses did a - maze___ us
"What you on?"___ To quote a phrase_ from ol' Satch - mo: "If you

more than Wil-liam Shake-speare's plays.__
got to ask you'll ne - ver know."__

We dig, ba-by,__ we
You swing, ba-by,__ you

dig you so;__
swing for me;__

We're gon - na miss you more than you could know.__
We vote you jazz-man of the cen-tu-ry.__

Your love and mu - sic, A mel-low mix;__
We'll al-ways sing your__ me - lo - dies,__

It's all we need-ed
And swing to your sweet

for some kicks.__ }
har - mo - nies.__ }

Sing-in', swing-in'; no life's com-plete__ Un-

-til it's known the rhy-thm of that El-ling-ton beat.__

Liv-in', lov-in' the

hu-man race,__ He made this cra - zy mixed-up world a swing-in' place.__

247

The Frim Fram Sauce

Words & Music by Joe Ricardel & Redd Evans

Medium bounce

I don't want french fried po-ta-toes,__ red ripe to-ma-toes,__

I'm ne-ver sa-tis-fied;__ I want the frim fram sauce with the

aus-sen fay__ with cha-fa-fa__ on the side.__ I don't want

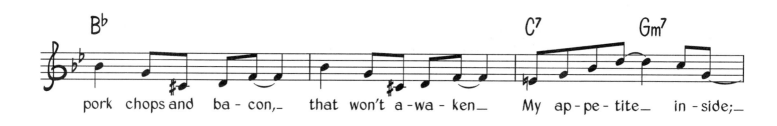

pork chops and ba-con,__ that won't a-wa-ken__ My ap-pe-tite__ in-side;__

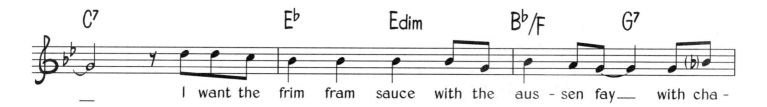

__ I want the frim fram sauce with the aus-sen fay__ with cha-

C⁷　Cm⁷ F⁷　B♭　　　Fm⁷　　B♭⁷　Fm⁷　　B♭⁷

-fa- fa— on the side.— Now a fel-low's— real-ly got to eat— and a

E♭　　B♭⁷aug　E♭　　Gm⁷　　C⁷　　　F　F♯dim

fel-low— should eat right,— Five will get you ten———— I'm gon-na

Gm⁷　　C¹³　　　F⁷　　　　B♭

feed my-self right— to-night!— I don't want fish-cakes and rye bread,—

　　　　　C⁷　　　Gm⁷　　C⁷

you heard what I said.— Wait-er, please serve— mine fried;— I want the

E♭　Edim　　B♭/F　G⁷　　C⁷　Cm⁷ F⁷　B♭

frim fram sauce with the aus-sen fay— with cha-fa-fa— on the side.—

The Girl From Ipanema (Garota De Ipanema)

Original Words by Vinicius De Moraes ★ English Lyric by Norman Gimbel ★ Music by Antonio Carlos Jobim

Bossa nova

Tall and tan and young_ and love-ly, the girl_ from I- pa-ne-
When she walks, she's like_ a sam-ba that swings_ so cool and sways_

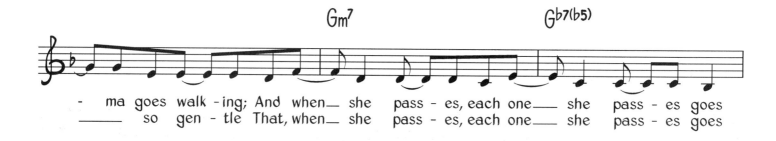

- ma goes walk-ing; And when_ she pass-es, each one_ she pass-es goes
_____ so gen-tle That, when_ she pass-es, each one_ she pass-es goes

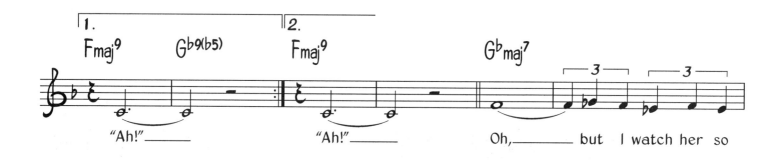

"Ah!"_____   "Ah!"_____   Oh,_____ but I watch her so

sad- ly._____   How_____ can I tell her I

love her?_____ Yes,_____ I would give my heart glad - ly;_____

___ But, each day when she walks to the sea, she looks straight a - head not at

me. Tall and tan and young___ and love - ly, the girl___ from I - pa - ne -

- ma goes walk -ing; And when___ she pass - es I smile,___ but she does - n't see.

She just does - n't see. No, she does - n't see._____

The Joint Is Jumpin'

Words by Andy Razaf & J.C. Johnson ★ Music by Thomas Waller

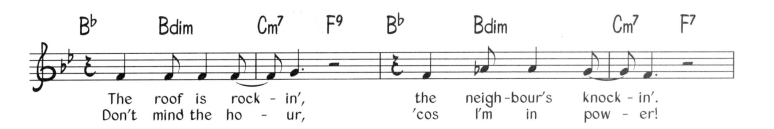

Bb   Bdim   Cm7   F9   Bb   Bdim   Cm7   F7

The roof is rock - in', the neigh-bour's knock - in'.
Don't mind the ho - ur, 'cos I'm in pow - er!

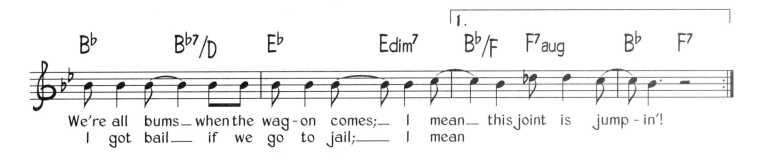

Bb   Bb7/D   Eb   Edim7   Bb/F   F7aug   Bb   F7

1.

We're all bums— when the wag-on comes;— I mean— this joint is jump - in'!
I got bail— if we go to jail;— I mean

2.

Bb   Eb7   F7   Bb   F7aug   Bb   Bdim   Cm7   F9

— this joint is jump - in'! This joint is jump - in',

Bb   Bdim   Cm7   F7   Bb   Bb7/Ab   Eb/G   Ebm/Gb

It's real-ly jump - in'! We're all bums— when the wag-on comes.— I mean—

Bb/F   F7aug   Bb   F7aug   Bb   Bb7/Ab

— this joint is jump - in'! *(Spoken:)* Don't give your

Eb/G   Ebm/Gb   Bb/F   Bbaug/F#   Gm7   C7(b9)   F7aug   Bb6

right name. *No, no, no! (Instrumental)*

The Last Time I Saw Paris

Music by Jerome Kern ★ Words by Oscar Hammerstein II

Medium tempo

The last time I saw Pa - ris, her heart was warm and

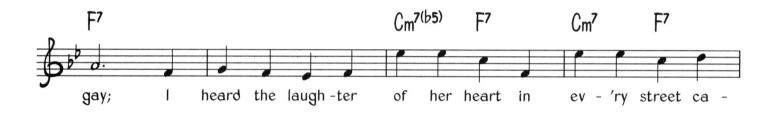

gay; I heard the laugh -ter of her heart in ev - 'ry street ca -

- fé. The last time I saw Pa - ris, her trees were dressed for

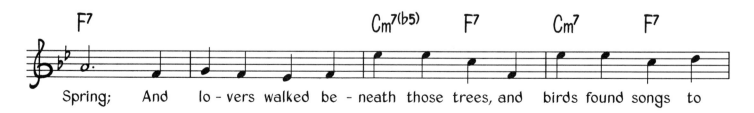

Spring; And lo -vers walked be - neath those trees, and birds found songs to

sing.　　I　dodged the same old　ta - xi - cabs that　I　had dodged for

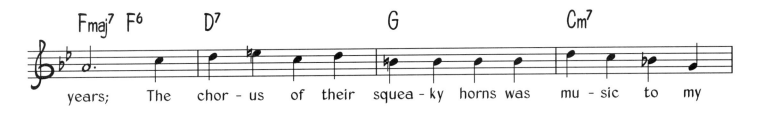

years;　The chor - us　of their squea - ky horns was　mu - sic to my

ears.　The　last time　I　saw　Pa - ris,　her　heart was warm and

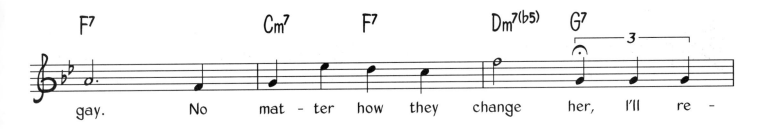

gay.　No　mat - ter how　they　change　her,　I'll　re -

- mem - ber her_____　　that　　way._____

255

The Best Is Yet To Come

Words by Carolyn Leigh ★ Music by Cy Coleman

Out of the tree of life___ I just picked me a plum;___

You came a-long and ev - 'ry-thing's start-in' to hum.___

Still it's a real good bet___ the best is yet to come.___

The best is yet to come___ and, babe, won't it be fine!___

You think you've seen the sun___ but you ain't seen it shine.___

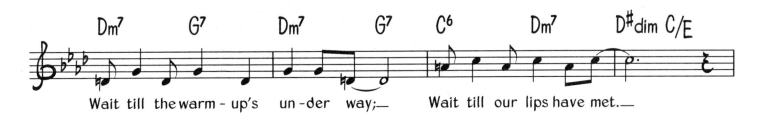

Dm7   G7   Dm7   G7   C6   Dm7   D#dim C/E

Wait till the warm-up's un-der way;— Wait till our lips have met.—

Dm7   G7   Dm7   G7   C6   Dm7   Eb13

Wait till you see that sun-shine day;— You ain't seen noth-in' yet!—

Ab   F7

The best is yet to come— and, babe, won't it be fine!———

Bb7   Eb7   1.   Optional repeat 2.
                        Ab   Ab

The best is yet to come,—come the day— you're mine.——— mine.

C7   C11(b9) Fm Db7 Fm   Db7   Fm Db7

Come— the day— you're mine,——— I'm gon-na teach you to fly.

Fdim   Eb7   Ab E7 Db7   E7   Ab E7 Bbm7 C7

We've on-ly tast-ed the wine;——We're gon-na drain the cup dry.—

Wait till your charms are ripe for these arms to sur - round;

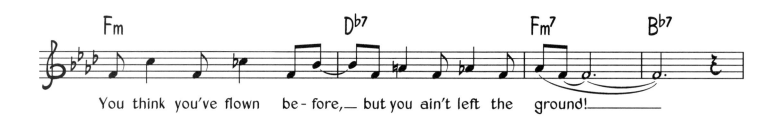

You think you've flown be - fore, but you ain't left the ground!

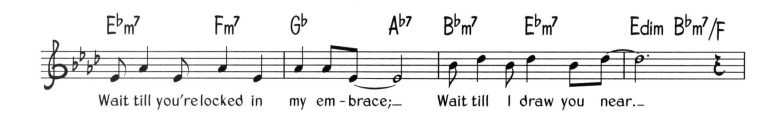

Wait till you're locked in my em - brace; Wait till I draw you near.

Wait till you see that sun - shine place; Ain't noth - in' like it here!

The best is yet to come and, babe, won't it be fine!

The best is yet to come, come the day you're mine.

The Mood I'm In

Words & Music by Pete King & Paul Francis Webster

1. I like to feel fan-cy free, I like to live young;
2. I like to hear op-'ra or I like to read Joyce;

I like the old mer-ry-go-round.
I'm not the pre-dic-ta-ble kind.

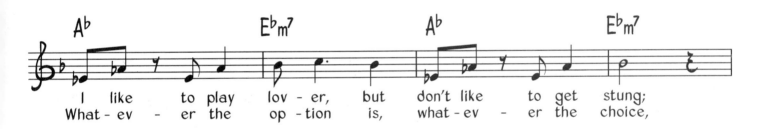

I like to play lov-er, but don't like to get stung;
What-ev-er the op-tion is, what-ev-er the choice,

I like my two feet on the ground. I may
I like to make up my own mind. If the

date a girl light-ly and kiss her po-lite-ly; But
choice were to break up or kiss her and make up, I'll

will she get un - der my skin?
try not to lead with my chin.

Well, my friends, it all de - pends on the

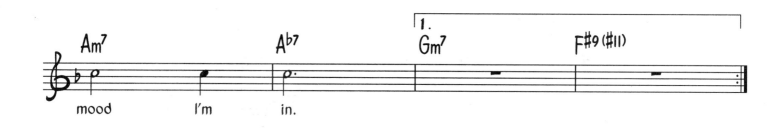

mood I'm in.

I may change, who can

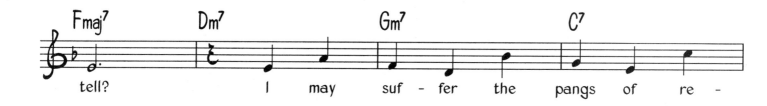

tell? I may suf - fer the pangs of re -

- morse. I may change 'neath the

spell Of that old ir - re - sis - ti - ble

force._____ But I'm gon - na root sin - gle, oh

don't look to find me Caught up in that ma - ri - tal

spin. Yet some - day I may sight one who

looks like the right one And waltz down the aisle with cha -

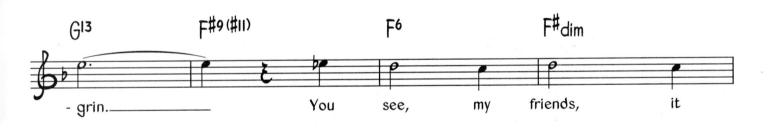
- grin._____ You see, my friends, it

all___ de - -pends on the mood I'm

in._____

Miles Davis

The Music Goes Round And Around

Words by Red Hodgson ★ Music by Edward Farley & Michael Riley

The Odd Couple

By Neal Hefti

Medium swing

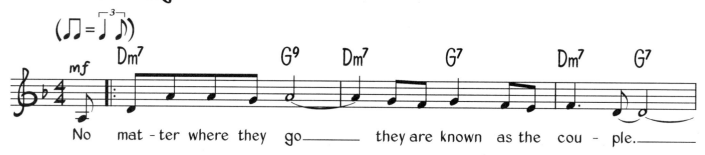

No mat-ter where they go____ they are known as the cou - ple.____

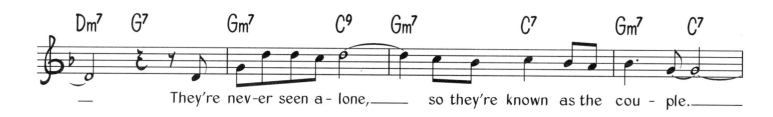

_ They're nev-er seen a - lone,____ so they're known as the cou - ple.____

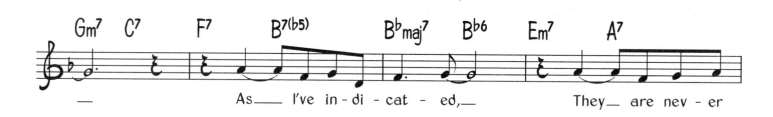

_ As___ I've in - di - cat - ed,___ They_ are nev - er

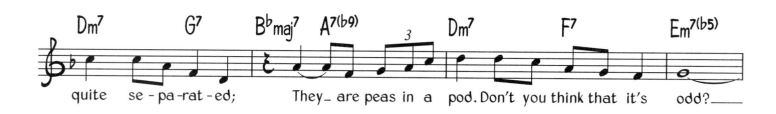

quite se - pa - rat - ed; They_ are peas in a pod. Don't you think that it's odd?____

_ Their hab - its, I con - fess,____ none can guess with the cou - ple.

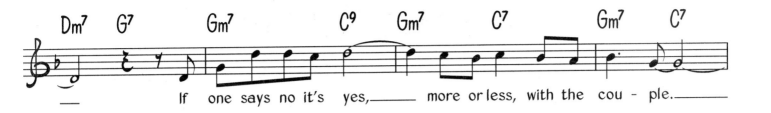

If one says no it's yes,____ more or less, with the cou - ple.____

But__ they're laugh pro -vok - ing;__ Yet__they real-ly don't

know they're jok -ing. Don't you find____when love is blind__ it's kind of odd!___

No odd!_____ Don't you think it's odd?____

Don't you think it's odd?___ Don't you think it's odd?_____

The Peanut Vendor

Words by Marion Sunshine & L. Wolfe Gilbert ★ Music by Moises Simons

- tive lit - tle strain, And as he goes by___ to you__ he'll say;___
- nut ven - dor's song. They all laugh with glee__ when he__ will say:___

__ "Big jum - bos, big doub - le ones. Come buy those
__ "They're roast - ed, no ti - - ny ones. They're toast - ed,

pea -nuts roast-ed to - day.__ Come try those fresh - ly roast-ed to-day!"___
pea -nuts hot in the shell.__ Come buy some, I eat more than I sell!"___

__ If you're look - ing for a mor - al to_____ this song,
__ If an ap - ple keeps the doc - tor from_____ your door,

2nd time: D.C. al Coda

Fif - ty mil - lion lit - tle mon -keys can't__ be wrong.
Pea - nuts ought to keep him from you ev - - er more.

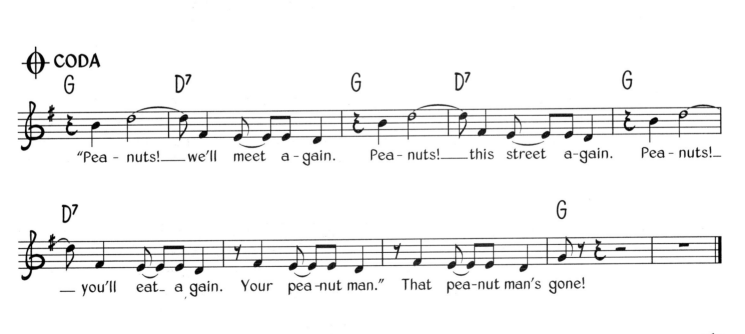

CODA

"Pea - nuts!__we'll meet a - gain. Pea - nuts!__this street a - gain. Pea - nuts!__

__ you'll eat_ a gain. Your pea -nut man." That pea -nut man's gone!

The Preacher

By Horace Silver

'Gospel' swing

Gath-er 'round and hear the Preach-er, hear the

Preach-er; Hear the Preach-er, preach-er man. They used to

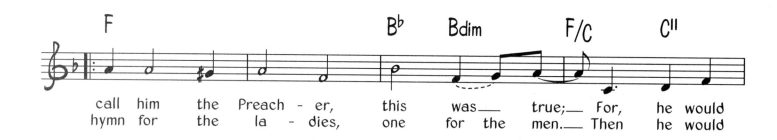

call him the Preach-er, this was true; For, he would
hymn for the la-dies, one for the men. Then he would

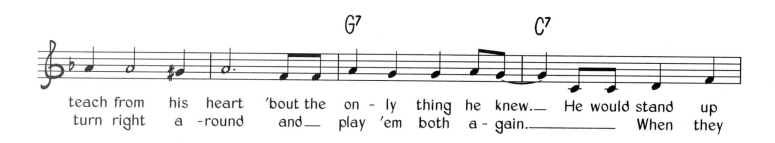

teach from his heart 'bout the on-ly thing he knew. He would stand up
turn right a-round and play 'em both a-gain. When they

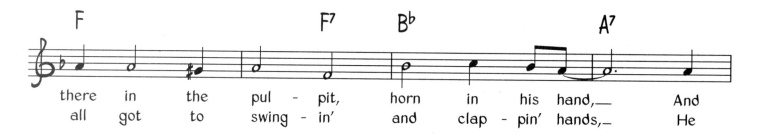

there in the pul-pit, horn in his hand, And
all got to swing-in' and clap-pin' hands, He

let that me - lo - dy take_ you to the Prom - ised Land._ He played one
had the swing - in' - est con - vo - ca - tion in_ the land._

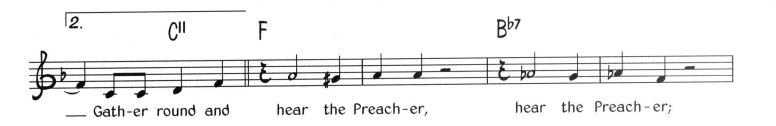

_ Gath - er round and hear the Preach - er, hear the Preach - er;

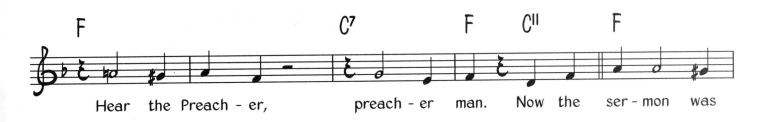

Hear the Preach - er, preach - er man. Now the ser - mon was

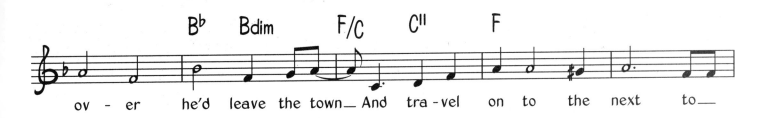

ov - er he'd leave the town_ And tra - vel on to the next to_

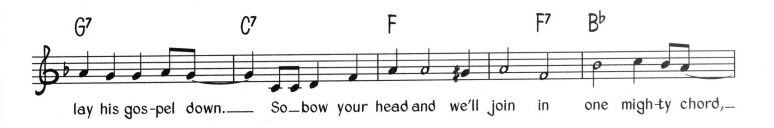

lay his gos - pel down._ So_ bow your head and we'll join in one migh - ty chord,_

_ To say a prayer for the Preach - er, gone to his_ re - ward._

The Sidewinder

By Lee Morgan

Medium fast

The side - - wind - er, The side - - wind - er;

He's a cool one, A - pril fool one! Dap - per

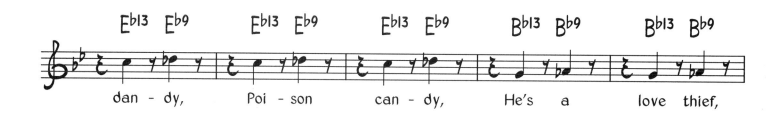

dan - dy, Poi - son can - dy, He's a love thief,

Hand - in' out grief; Quick as quick - sand, Sleight - of -

- hand man. Don't you play his game!

The side - - wind - er, He ain't got no pi - ty at all;—

Bb13 Bb9   Bb13 Bb9

The side - - wind - er,   His big kick is mak - in' 'em fall.__

Eb13 Eb9   Eb13 Eb9

The side - - - wind - er,   Don't trust him half as much as

Bb7 Bb13 Bb9   Bb13 Bb9

you would a snake,   A rat - tle snake! The side - - wind - er,

Cm7 Gm7   Cm7 Gm7

Don't let him get you,   Don't let him get you!   The side - - wind - er,

Cm7   B7(b5)   Bb7 Bb13 Bb9   Bb13 Bb9

The side-wind-er's call-ing your name.__   Don't you   play his

Repeat to fade

Bb13 Bb9   Bb13 Bb9

game! *(Instrumental)*   The side - - wind - er.

The Song Is You

Music by Jerome Kern ★ Words by Oscar Hammerstein II

Medium slow

I hear mu-sic when I look at you;— A beau-ti-ful theme of ev-'ry dream I ev-er

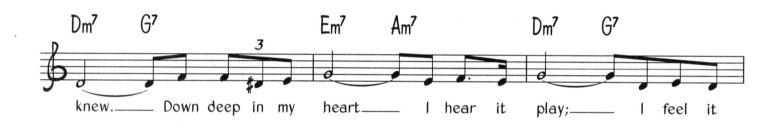

knew.— Down deep in my heart— I hear it play;— I feel it

start,— then melt a - way. I hear mu-sic when I touch your

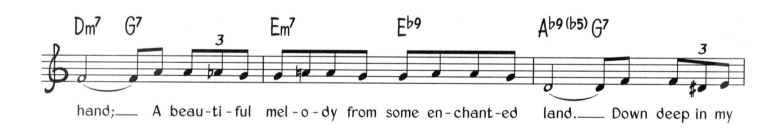

hand;— A beau-ti-ful mel-o-dy from some en-chant-ed land.— Down deep in my

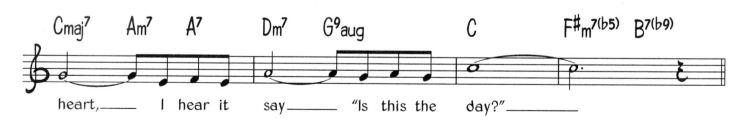

heart,— I hear it say— "Is this the day?"—

I a-lone___ have heard this love-ly strain; I a-lone___ have heard this

glad re-frain. Must it be___ for ev-er in-side of me?___ Why can't I

let it go,___why can't I let you know? Why can't I let you know the song my heart would

sing;___ That beau-ti-ful rhap-so-dy of love and youth and spring?___ The mu-sic is

sweet,___ the words are true.___ The song is you.___

There'll Be A Hot Time In The Old Town Tonight

Words & Music by Theodore Metz

Medium fast

When you hear dem a - bells go ding ling, ling,

All join 'round and __ sweet - ly you must sing; And when the

verse am through, in the cho - rus all join in. There'll be a

hot time in the old town to - night. __

Time After Time

Words by Sammy Cahn ★ Music by Jule Styne

Too Close For Comfort

Words & Music by Larry Holofcener, George Weiss & Jerry Bock

Medium swing

Be wise, be smart, be - have my heart; Don't up -

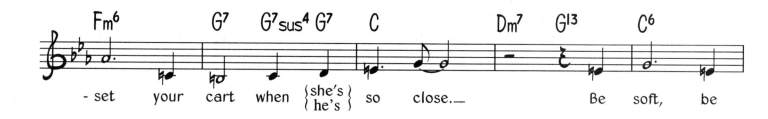

- set your cart when {she's / he's} so close.— Be soft, be

sweet, but be dis - creet, Don't go off your beat. {She's / He's} too

close for com - fort. Too close, too__ close for com - fort,

please not a - gain;__ Too close, too__ close to know just

when to say when.___ Be firm, be fair, be sure, be -

- ware; On your guard, take care while there's such temp - ta - tion.

One thing leads_ to an-oth - er; Too late to___ run for cov - er,

To ✛ Coda   *D. 𝄋 al Coda*

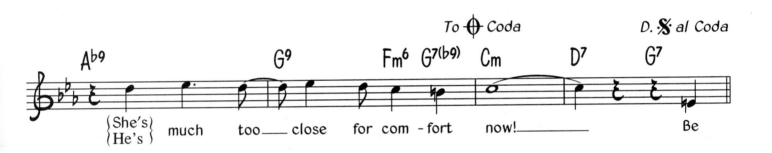

{She's} {He's} much too___ close for com - fort now!_____ Be

✛ **CODA**

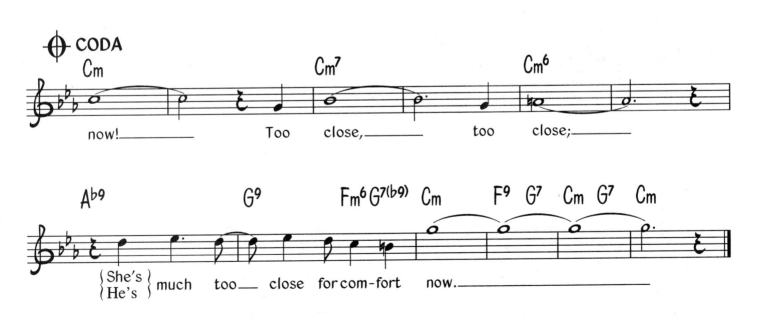

now!_____ Too close,___ too close;_____

{She's} {He's} much too___ close for com-fort now._____

Time's A-Wastin'

Medium swing

Words & Music by Duke Ellington, Mercer Ellington & Don George

Undecided

Words by Sid Robin ★ Music by Charles Shavers

First you say you do and then you don't,— And then you say you will and
Now you want to play, and then it's no;— And when you say you'll stay, that's

then you won't.—
when you go.— } You're un-de-ci-ded now, so what are you gon-na do?—

I've been sit-ting on a fence and it does-n't make much sense, 'Cos you

keep me in sus-pense and you know it.— Then you pro-mise to re-turn. When you

don't, I real-ly burn. Well, I guess I'll nev-er learn, and I show it.—

If you've got a heart and if you're kind,— Then don't keep us a-part; make

up your mind.— You're un-de-ci-ded now, so what are you gon-na do?—

Waiting For The Robert E. Lee

Words by L. Wolfe Gilbert ★ Music by Lewis F. Muir

Waltz For Debby

Music by Bill Evans ★ Words by Gene Lees

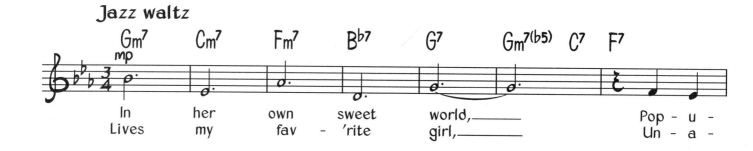

In her own sweet world,_____ Pop-u-
Lives my own fav-'rite girl,_____ Un-a-

-lat-ed by dolls and clowns and a prince and a big pur-ple
-ware of the wor-ried frowns that we

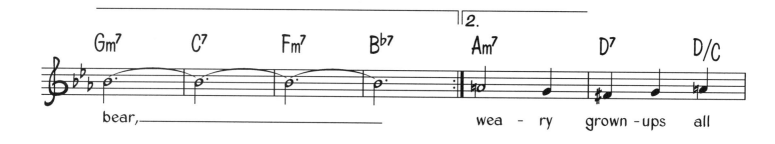

bear,_____ wea-ry grown-ups all

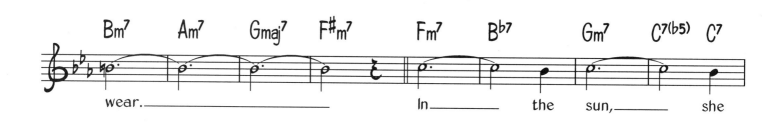

wear._____ In_____ the sun,_____ she

danc-es to si-lent mu-sic, Songs that are spun of gold some-

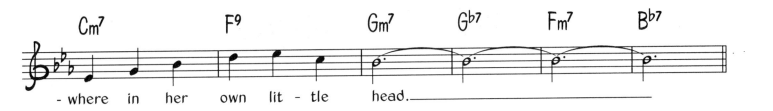

Cm⁷ — F⁹ — Gm⁷ — G♭⁷ — Fm⁷ — B♭⁷

- where in her own lit - tle head._____

Gm⁷ — Cm⁷ — Fm⁷ — B♭⁷ — G⁷ — Gm⁷⁽ᵇ⁵⁾ C⁷ F⁷ — B♭⁷

One day, all too soon,_____ She'll grow up and she'll

E♭⁷ — A♭maj⁷ — Fm⁷⁽ᵇ⁵⁾ — B♭⁷ — B♭⁷/A♭ Gm⁷ — C⁷⁽ᵇ⁵⁾

leave her dolls and her prince and her sil - ly old bear._____

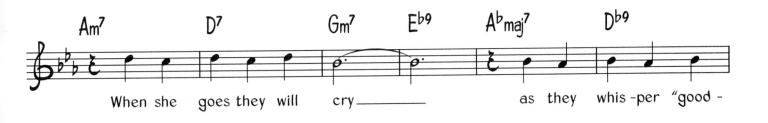

Am⁷ — D⁷ — Gm⁷ E♭⁹ — A♭maj⁷ — D♭⁹

When she goes they will cry_____ as they whis -per "good -

Cm — Cm⁷/B♭ F⁷/A — A♭dim — E♭⁶/G — G♭dim

- bye."_____ They will miss her, I fear, but then

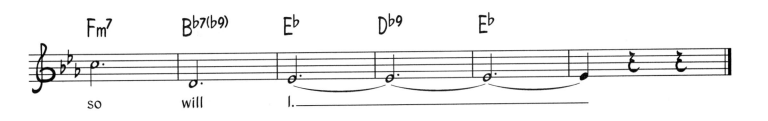

Fm⁷ — B♭⁷⁽ᵇ⁹⁾ E♭ — D♭⁹ — E♭

so will I._____

Wave

Words & Music by Antonio Carlos Jobim

Bossa nova

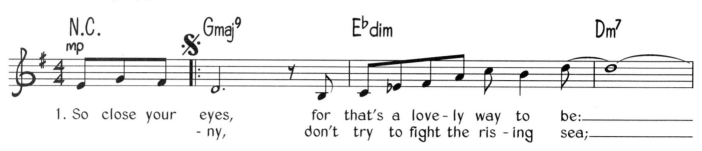

1. So close your eyes, for that's a love-ly way to be:___
- ny, don't try to fight the ris-ing sea;___

___ A-ware___ of things___ your heart___ a-lone___ was meant___ to see.___
___ Don't fight___ the moon,___ the stars___ a-bove___ and don't___ fight me.___

The fun-da-men-tal lone-li-ness goes___ when-ev-er two can dream a dream to-geth-

-er.___ 2. You can't de-___ When I saw you first, the time was

half   past three.____   When____ your eyes met mine,   it   was   e -

- ter - ni - ty._____   By   now   we   know   the   wave is on its way to   be.__

_____ Just catch_ the   wave,_don't   be__   a - fraid__ of lov - ing   me._

___   The   fun - da - men - tal   lone - li - ness goes_ when - ev - er

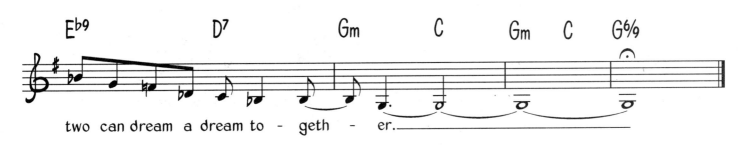

two can dream a dream to - geth - er._____

Well You Needn't (It's Over Now)

Music by Thelonious Monk ★ English Lyric by Mike Ferro

Medium swing

You're talk-in' so sweet, well you need -n't. You say you won't cheat, well you
play-in' a game, well you need -n't. It's more of the same, well you

need -n't. You're tap-pin' your feet, well you need -n't. It's
need -n't. You're com-in' up lame, well you need -n't. It's

ov - er now, it's ov - er now. You're dress-in' with class, well you
ov - er now, it's ov - er now. You're bend -in' my ear, well you

need -n't. You're hold - in' your sass, well you need -n't. You
need -n't. You're call - in' me dear, well you need -n't. You're

think you're a gas, well you need -n't. It's ov - er now, it's ov - er
act - in' sin - cere, well you need -n't. It's ov - er now, it's ov - er

now. / now.
It's ov-er now, it's ov-er now. You / Don't

had your fun, so take a bow. You ought-a know, you lost the glow. The
want a scene, don't need a row. You had your day, a ma-ti-nee. You

beat is slow, the shad-ows grow; The lights are low, it's time to go. Let's
had to stray; you know they say "You're gon-na play, you got to pay." So

close the show down!__ You're tak-in' off weight, well you need n't. You're
find a way out!__ You say that you'll try, well you need-n't. You

look-in' just great, well you need-n't. You're set-tin' the bait, well you
say you won't lie, well you need-n't. You're start-in' to cry, well you

need-n't. It's ov-er now, it's ov-er now. You're now.
need-n't. It's ov-er now, it's ov-er

287

When You Smile

Words & Music by William Salter & Ralph MacDonald

Medium fast

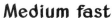

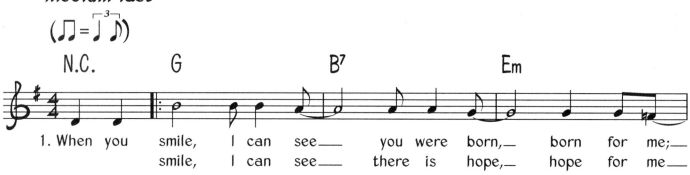

1. When you smile, I can see____ you were born,____ born for me;
   smile, I can see____ there is hope,____ hope for me____

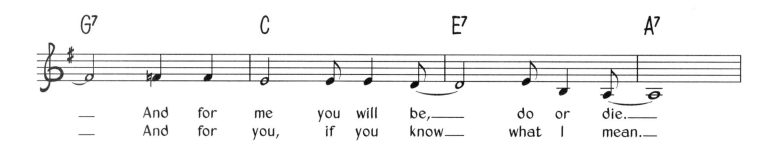

____ And for me you will be,____ do or die.____
____ And for you, if you know____ what I mean.____

Oh ba-by let me hold____ you;____ You make me want to hold____ you____
I'm gon-na sock it to____ you;____ I'm gon-na rock it to____ you____

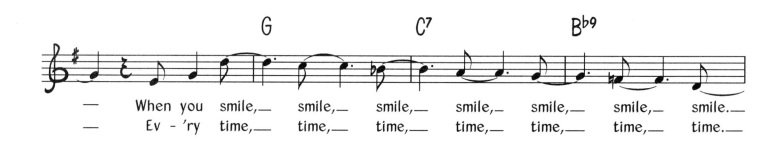

____ When you smile,____ smile,____ smile,____ smile,____ smile,____ smile,____ smile.
____ Ev-'ry time,____ time,____ time,____ time,____ time,____ time,____ time.

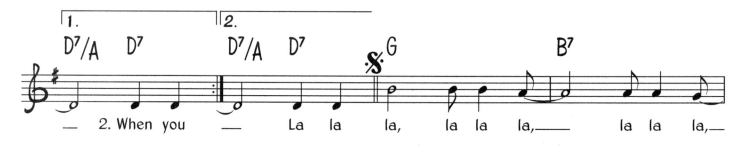

____ 2. When you ____ La la la, la la la,____ la la la,

289

When You're Smiling

Words & Music by Mark Fisher, Joe Goodman & Larry Shay

Who's Sorry Now?

Music by Ted Snyder ★ Words by Bert Kalmer & Harry Ruby

Witchcraft

Words by Carolyn Leigh ★ Music by Cy Coleman

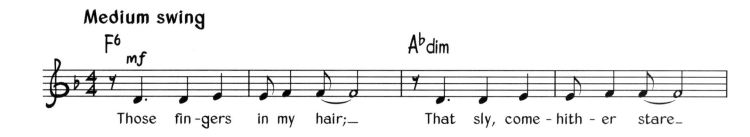

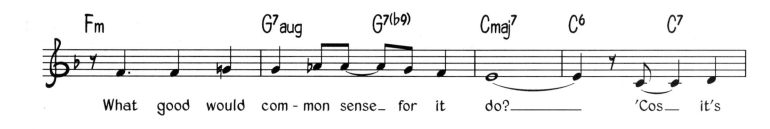

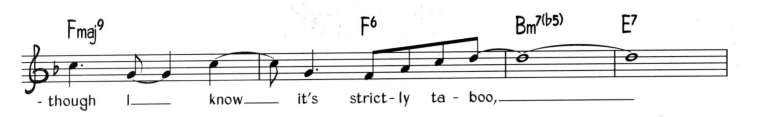

-though I____ know____ it's strict-ly ta - boo,____

When you a - rouse the need_ in me, My heart says "Yes in-deed"_ in me,

"Pro - ceed with what you're lead - in' me to!"_____

It's such an an - cient pitch,_ But one I would - n't switch;_

'Cos there's no nic - er witch_ than you!____

Wooftie

By Chubby Jackson

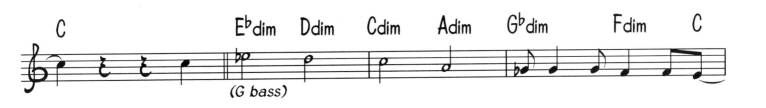

(G bass)

(G bass)

Yardbird Suite

By Charlie Parker

Yes Indeed (A Jive Spiritual)

Words & Music by Sy Oliver

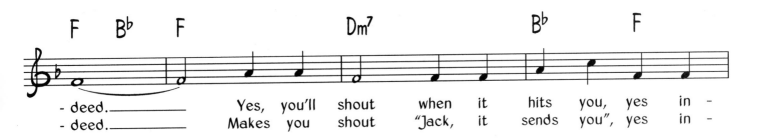

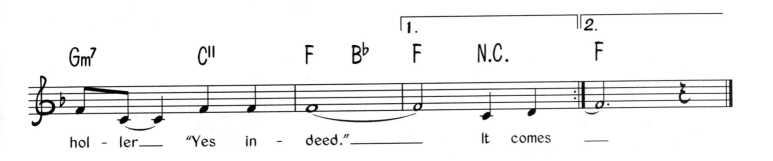

You Always Hurt The One You Love

Words & Music by Doris Fisher & Allan Roberts

You al - -ways hurt the one you

love, The one___ you should -n't hurt at all.___

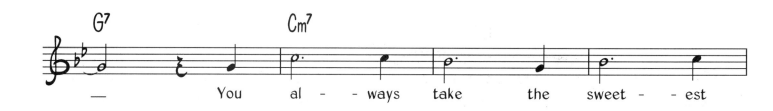

___ You al - -ways take the sweet - -est

rose, And crush___ it till the pet - -als fall.___

You al - - ways break the kind - - est

heart, With a has - ty word you can't re - call.____

So if I broke your heart last

night, It's be - cause____ I love you most of

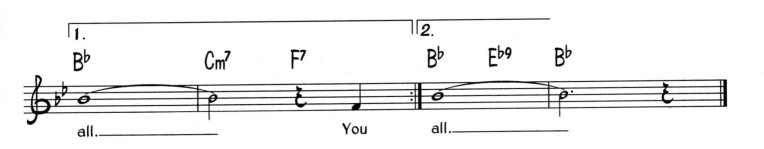

all._____ You all._____

Zambesi

Music by Nico Carstens & Anton De Waal ★ Revised Lyric by Bob Grover

Medium fast

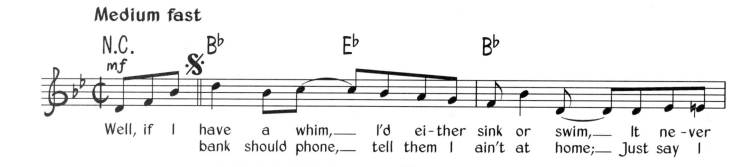

Well, if I have a whim,— I'd ei-ther sink or swim,— It ne-ver
bank should phone,— tell them I ain't at home;— Just say I

real-ly seems to mat-ter ei-ther way; And if a bill comes in,— just throw it
packed my plas-tic bag and went a-way. As for the land-lord's rent,— I spent it

in the bin,— Be-cause I'm sure to get some more a-no-ther day.
on a tent;— So if he's ask-ing ques-tions you'll know what to say.

To Coda ⊕

Zam-be-si, Zam-be-si, Zam-be-si, Zam, I'm on— my way;

Zam-be-si, Zam-be-si, Zam-be-si, Zam! I

ought to face life's com-pli-ca-tions but I have-n't got the in-cli-na-tion, And I
when the bai-liff comes, ex-plain_ to him I have-n't got a thing to give_ to him, But

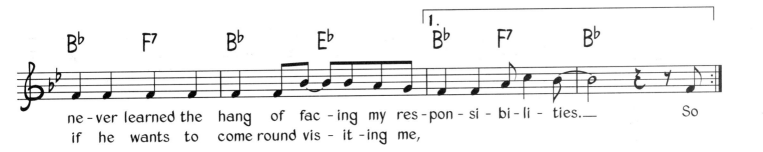

ne-ver learned the hang of fac-ing my res-pon-si-bi-li-ties.__ So
if he wants to come round vis-it-ing me,

this is where I'll be.__ Zam - be - si, Zam - be - si,

Zam - be - si, Zam, I'm on__ my way; Zam - be - si,

D. S al Coda

Zam - be - si, Zam - be - si, Zam! Well if my

✛ CODA

Zam - be - si, Zam - be - si, Zam - be - si, Zam!

Yesterdays

Music by Jerome Kern ★ Words by Otto Harbach

Medium slow

Yes - ter - days,___ yes - ter - days:___
youth was mine,___ truth was mine;

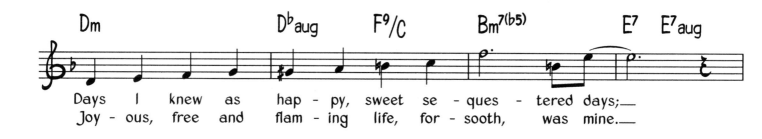

Days I knew as hap - py, sweet se - ques - tered days;___
Joy - ous, free and flam - ing life, for - sooth, was mine.___

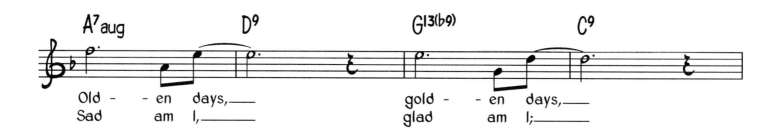

Old - - en days,___ gold - - en days,___
Sad am I,_____ glad am I;

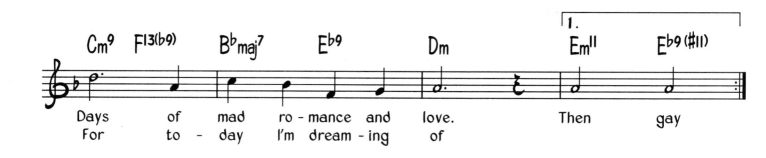

Days of mad ro - mance and love. Then gay
For to - day I'm dream - ing of

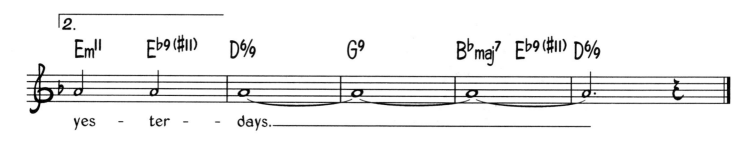

yes - ter - - days._____

Get real ...

Play the world's greatest music instantly with these bumper collections of jazz and blues numbers, all-time great songs and favourite classics.

All books are presented in clear, easy-to-read melody line arrangements by Jack Long, with chord symbols and lyrics (where appropriate).

The Real Book of Jazz

Over 190 great jazz standards including A Foggy Day; Ain't Misbehavin'; Call Me Irresponsible; Caravan; Django; Don't Blame Me; Fascinating Rhythm; Honeysuckle Rose; I'm Beginning To See The Light; In The Still Of The Night; Just One Of Those Things; Lullaby Of Birdland; Night Flight; Oh, Lady, Be Good; Opus One; Petite Fleur; Satin Doll; So Nice; Straight No Chaser; That Old Black Magic; Waltz For Debbie; Wave and Who's Sorry Now?

Order No. AM952435

The Real Book of Blues

A superb compilation of 225 big blues numbers including After You've Gone; Black Coffee; Blues Stay Away From Me; Body And Soul; Chelsea Bridge; Crazy Man Blues; Dust My Broom; Frankie And Johnny; Georgia On My Mind; Here's That Rainy Day; How Insensitive; I Ain't Got Nobody; Lazybones; Li'l Darlin'; Memphis Blues; Misty; More Than You Know; Singing The Blues; Sunny; Take These Chains From My Heart; When Sunny Gets Blue and Worried Man Blues.

Order No. AM952446

The Real Book of Great Songs

An essential collection of over 200 all-time great songs including A Woman In Love; Amapola; Arrivederci Roma; Be Mine Tonight; Carolina Moon; El Cumbanchero; Fools Rush In; Getting To Know You; I Left My Heart In San Francisco; London By Night; She; Spanish Eyes; Strangers In The Night; The Twelfth Of Never; This Guy's In Love With You; Tonight; Unchained Melody; Unforgettable; What Kind Of Fool Am I and Yesterday When I Was Young.

Order No. AM952468

The Real Book of Favourite Classics

Well-known classical themes from over 60 of the world's greatest composers including Air On The 'G' String (J.S. Bach); Ode To Joy (Beethoven); Themes from 'Carmen' (Bizet); Hungarian Dances Nos. 4, 5 & 6 (Brahms); Prelude in C Minor Op.28 No.20 (Chopin); Clair De Lune (Debussy); O Sole Mio (Di Capua); Nimrod (Elgar); Entry Of The Gladiators (Fučik); March from 'Scipione' (Handel); Liebestraum (Liszt); Plaisir d'Amour (Martini); Wedding March (Mendelssohn); Theme from Symphony No.40 (Mozart); Ave Maria (Schubert); Radetzky March (J. Strauss); Theme from Piano Concerto No.1 (Tchaikovsky) and Themes from 'The Four Seasons' (Vivaldi).

Order No. AM952479

Jack Long

Jack Long's career began in his teens when he played piano with many luminaries of the British jazz world. He first came to the attention of the music industry in the 1970s as a big band arranger with his transcriptions of some of the classic American recordings in this genre - all still widely played today.

He has since acted as musical director for several well-known entertainers, notably Ray Ellington, and worked as a session pianist and accompanist, while combining a parallel career in contemporary 'serious' music, editing for a number of publishers, including Chester and Novello, and composers such as Alexander Goehr. His own compositions have featured in film and television productions along with a wide range of original material for innumerable singers, producers such as Bruce Welch, and ensembles of all descriptions, including the National Youth Jazz Orchestra.

An experienced arranger, both in broadcasting and recording, his credits range from small studio groups to 150-piece orchestra and chorus.

Exclusive Distributors:
Music Sales Limited
8/9 Frith Street,
London W1V 5TZ, England.

Music Sales Pty Limited
120 Rothschild Avenue,
Rosebery, NSW 2018,
Australia.

Order No. AM952435
ISBN 0-7119-7334-2

Music compiled and arranged by Jack Long
Music processed by Enigma Music Production Services
Cover design by Chloë Alexander
Photographs courtesy of London Features International
Printed and bound in the USA.

Your Guarantee of Quality
As publishers, we strive to produce every book to the highest commercial
standards.
The music has been freshly engraved and the book has been carefully
designed to minimise awkward page turns and to make playing from it a
real pleasure.
Particular care has been given to specifying acid-free, neutral-sized paper
made from pulps which have not been elemental chlorine bleached. This
pulp is from farmed sustainable forests and was produced with special
regard for the environment.
Throughout, the printing and binding have been planned to ensure a
sturdy, attractive publication which should give years of enjoyment.
If your copy fails to meet our high standards, please inform us and we will
gladly replace it.

Music Sales' complete catalogue describes thousands of titles and is
available in full colour sections by subject, direct from Music Sales Limited.
Please state your areas of interest and send a cheque/postal order for
£1.50 for postage to: Music Sales Limited, Newmarket Road,
Bury St. Edmunds, Suffolk IP33 3YB.

www.musicinprint.com